Banana Split Misfit

Unravel as You Travel

Tyke Fortier

destinēe

Banana Split Misfit – Unravel as You Travel
By Tyke Fortier
Copyright © 2020 by Tyke Fortier

Author: Tyke Fortier
Publisher: Destinee Media, www.destineemedia.com
Cover and interior illustrations: T.P. Wright
ISBN: 978-1-938367-60-1

TABLE OF CONTENTS

Acknowledgements iv

1. Nepal 1

2. Kathmandu...10

3. Buddhist Monastery...25

4. New Delhi, India...35

5. Burma-Thailand-Malaysia-Singapore 45

6. Bali...50

7. Bombay...62

8. Goa...71

9. Goa Full Moon..81

10. Jaipur...96

11. Kashmir – Houseboat 113

12. Srinagar.. 125

13. Cairo.. 133

14. Cyprus.. 145

15. Israel 150

16. Rome 168

17. Miss Evinrude.. 188

18. Spaghetti Western 198

19. Florence... 209

20. Paris... 217

21. North Africa – Tunisia.. 226

22. Algeria – Sahara Desert 230

23. Niger – Sahara Desert... 237

24. Nigeria 245

25. Ibiza, Spain.. 253

Photos of My Travels 261

About the Author 268

ACKNOWLEDGEMENTS

First, I want to thank Ralph McCall and his lovely wife Catherine, my dear friends and co-publishers at Destinée Media! You not only triggered the idea for me to write this book, but you have given me vital support, encouragement, and help! I can't thank you enough for igniting my motivation to tell my story. I am also forever grateful for your hands-on help designing my cover, formatting this book, providing a link on your website, and more! Thank you, Catherine, for your insightful suggestions that helped me focus on the direction of this book's content and for laughing out loud while reading it!

Thanks to my brother and mentor, Spike Fortier. You have been my foremost encourager, cheering me on page by page and supplying stellar advice. You have mentored me not only with this book but in life. . .since childhood! Your wit and kindness have always inspired me, teaching me to laugh at myself.

Thanks to my cousin, Fran Fortier, who sparked my desire to leave New Orleans and head to Paris, where she was perfecting her French! Your interest, enthusiasm, and word-smith skills have been crucial to this book.

Thanks to Joey McLean, my ex-roommate and close friend, for diving into my project with your alluring "eagle-eyes". . . .as well as helping me fill a few pages of this book with our humorous antics together in Morocco.

Thanks to my friend Elaine Winter for proofreading this book when it was raw and quite illegible and for being such a welcomed cheerleader! You are a real angel who miraculously deciphered my book, page by page, as I was writing it.

Thanks to T.P. Wright, the innovative, talented artist who brilliantly caught my quirky attitude and managed to get it down on paper.

Thanks to Dave Screaton for his heavenly work of storing my manuscript on a cloud - chapter by chapter, including all the rewrites.

Thanks to my husband, Peter, for removing so many stones from my path and always believing in me and my projects! Your patience and support through the years have warmed my heart and held me up!

The two most important days of your life are the day you are born and the day you find out why.

—Mark Twain

1. NEPAL

As the elephant inched in closer to the rhino, persuaded by a whack on the head from my driver, my fight or flight mechanism activated, and I could hear a bellow from the depths of my adrenaline hormones screeching "NO, NO, NO – STOP, EEEEK." We had reached the point of no return! The rhino's ears shifted and twitched, then the alerting signal of his vacating bladder. . . .then the CHARGE!

I guess I was seeking a thrill, or why on earth would I have accepted the offer from that anemic looking Latin Professor from Turin? Over a lukewarm cup of *chai* at a hippie café in downtown Kathmandu, Vittorio invited me to join him on a day trip to the Chitwan Forest in the Nepalese jungle. He described, with Italian passion, "There is an elephant-powered lumber camp, and we can ride on the work elephants after they finish their tree pulling chores." I think that's what he said - I didn't understand much Italian and only had two sketchy years of high school Latin.

Vittorio resembled Woody Allen. He was about three inches shorter than my five foot nine and had no apparent muscles, so I decided he was a safe, calculated risk. I was not disappointed. You see, by the early 1970s, a multi-hued stream of near-penniless travelers had created a pulsating road to Kathmandu; however, Vittorio was on a sabbatical from an honest job and even had a Land Rover! He was a respectful, cultured mature man in his 30's and of some means. Most importantly, Vittorio thought I looked like a cross between the famous angular model, Veruschke, and the singer-songwriter, Carly Simon. So I knew, for a fact, he was a man of sound judgment.

Now back to the jungle. As fortune would have it, I grew up in the buckle of the ozone belt, outside of New Orleans, and my limbs had grown extra long. Lanky legs are essential when you straddle a wide elephant - if not, you end up in an awkward ballet-type split position atop a moving mass. Who would imagine that elephants hit top speeds of nearly twenty miles per hour? Due to their footfall pattern, while walking and running, a bouncing motion is created. Not a relaxing ride with only a rough rope to cling to and no stirrups. Since my hair was a yard long of matted, dreadful locks, I kept getting snagged, resulting in whiplash from nearby trees, vines and other green stuff. I was glad I wore my bell-bottom jeans and a long-sleeved camouflage t-shirt. Dually, I could blend into the forest and also avoid brush burns.

When I sensed at one point that my over-zealous driver was out of control; I heard myself praying my childhood prayer audibly in fast forward, "Now I lay me down to sleep, I pray the Lord my soul to keep, if I should die before I wake, I pray the Lord my soul to take." It was a cunning strategy. The rhino slowed his pace and seemed to lose interest. Batsa, my chauffeur, and I had bonded in our near-death experience. He was sun-baked, as black as a moonless night, with the slim physique of a fourteen-year-old, but was obviously about my age. I was almost disappointed to dismount and be grounded so Vittorio could have his turn.

With only a few scrapes and scratches, I was ready for the next thrill. However, my eight months of stimulating travel were not only to seek thrills but also to nourish my spirit and soul. Our hippie motto was, `if it feels good, do it' and that seemed to make perfect sense from someone teethed on the rejection of conventional values. Anti-establishmentarianism was our battered battle cry! However, that now seemed a bit trite, and I was seeking something more profound to give my life some sort of significance.

We rattled back to Kathmandu in Vittorio's vintage Land Rover, whizzing past worn out temples and Tibetan Monuments (*Stupas*) with strings of faded prayer flags rippling overhead. I spent days exploring those ancient temples inch by inch. I was fascinated by the local Buddhist monastery, where four generations of monks were seated in neat rows of varying disinterest, chanting in drowsy unison, *om mani padme hum*. It is the mantra of the Compassionate Buddha that calms fears, soothes concerns, and heals broken hearts. I planned on an in-depth study of Tibetan Buddhism when time allowed.

Fortunately, my paternal grandparents had divorced before I was born. That wise move ejected my French-descended family from its centuries of allegiance to the Pope and the Catholic Church, consequently liberating me from the strict rules that seemed to convert almost everything I did into sin. My playmates and peers suffered the consequences, but I escaped tedious penance by attending the local Methodist Church . . . until I was fourteen.

Those days, the dress code included high heeled pumps, a demure dress, white gloves, and a hat. I felt Bohemian, singing Joan Baez ballads and listening to Bob Dylan's nasal, activist off-tune melodies. I simply didn't fit into their dress code or mindset.

I was now liberated and free to search for a higher power that fit my needs and lifestyle. The Beatles had a personal trainer in India and visited their Hindu spiritual teacher, *Guru Maharishi*. I could relate to their spiritual search. What attracted me to Kathmandu was religious freedom, the smooth blending of Hinduism, Tibetan Buddhism, and counter-culture Hedonism. They were belief systems and religious traditions that flourished side by side in peaceful harmony.

That smogless small metropolis, nestled in a lush green valley, surrounded by the mammoth Himalayas, was an absolute dream for a Southern Belle who had grown up beneath sea level. There was one man-made hill in Audubon Park, near the local zoo in New Orleans, so kids could experience the inertia of running upward and downward. My fantasy was to go trekking in the foothills of the mighty Himalayas, spurred on by reading Hillary's *High Adventure* when I was a dreamy teen.

Wouldn't you know, my pale, auburn-haired Italian friend Vittorio had organized a five-day trekking trip into those very foothills! He had a tent, cooking utensils, food, and an experienced Sherpa guide. He invited me to join their expedition, with no strings attached. I let out a yelp and then ran out to locate the busy office that processed trekking permits. I also needed a reliable pair of hiking boots.

Having never walked more than a mile, I agreed that no-one with any sense walks in Louisiana with such oppressive heat, humidity and snakes. You drive from point to point in your air-conditioned coupe, swim, water ski, sail, boat, or work out in refrigerated gyms. I found the perfect trekking boots at the supply shop and splurged on a knit cap with a fluffy pom-pom for chilly nights. I also snapped up a small pickaxe, just in case. I was too wet behind the ears to think that twelve hours a day hiking up and down mountains might prove challenging. I jammed my backpack with a pair of jeans, two t-shirts, undies, a toothbrush, a towel, and my good luck book, *The Power of Positive Thinking*, by Norman Vincent Peale.

I didn't consider myself superstitious, but I wore my silver Mary medal that I won at camp when I was nine. Mary was coated with blue enamel, and on the flip side was written in relief, "I am a Catholic, call a priest." I well deserved winning that Mary medal in the talent contest at Camp Saint Gertrude. I had accomplished it by cleverly climbing a nearby tree, imitating Comanche ceremonial chants with emotion, as well as some shrill, Wood Warbler bird calls. Ah yes, I then grabbed my good luck flip flops, a rabbit's foot, and my Tibetan ring.

Along with the stoic Sherpa, Vittorio picked me up at daybreak in his trusty, rusty Land Rover. We bounced and gyrated northwest for nearly five hours before arriving at the starting point of our trek, nine miles short of the village of Pokhara. Our journey along the river bank was dotted with rural Nepalese villages. Each kid we passed started jumping up and down, waving enthusiastically, and wearing a smile that covered their little face. I wished I'd had a big sack of candy to give to each one we saw. Tourism was still a novelty for rural Nepalese in those days.

* * *

As we approached our starting point, the famed Everest range was coming into clear view, and I felt humbled by the magnitude of God's awesome handiwork - what a staggering sight to behold! As I breathed in the dry, piercing, invigorating air, I felt like a wonder woman on her next mission to save the world. I felt invincible – I was invincible!

I was wearing the safari shorts I bought in St. Tropez when I first arrived in Europe, realizing it would be a great way to keep my long legs bronzed and allow my knees more leeway when climbing steep terrain. I wore my green "lucky" long-sleeved t-shirt since it coordinated with my shorts and seemed appropriate for a nature hike. My backpack was hefty, but I was feeling capable, and besides, it would give me momentum. . . .at least downhill.

The Sherpa looked to the horizon, lifted his strong hand into the air and pointed, "One, two, three mountains, we sleep." I wondered if that was a coded message or if he meant we had to climb and descend three mountains before we could call it a day.

After four hours of meandering through a valley, we started the ascent. But first, we had some chewy local cheese and stale bread with lukewarm water to coax it down. I peeled off my trekking boots to inspect the motive for "on fire" feet. I had thirteen blisters, but the soles of my feet were flawless. I tossed the boots and decided to flip flop my way towards heaven. Walking eleven-twelve hours daily, I discovered that repeating mantras kept me in step and gave me stamina. The vibrations from my repeated *Oms* stabilized my metabolism. I tried to settle into that state of mindlessness as I did with guided meditations during my Yoga classes. I breathed in light and love 2-3-4 and breathed out negativity 2-3-4. It was dusk when a sole trekker passed us heading downward. With flailing arms, Vittorio shouted, "Hey, Ian, why are you going backward?"

Ian was a tall, virile, athletic-looking chap with a guitar strapped to his backpack. I was praying he might join our expedition. This chisel-chinned sculpture confessed, "I got acrophobia at the swinging bridge!" He buried his head into his hands and then informed us that he glanced into the bottomless gorge and saw that the bridge was missing slats, and the entire length was swaying recklessly in a full-force gale. Small scale Vittorio hugged Ian sympathetically, Italian style, and our stoic Sherpa Nawang shrugged without slowing his pace.

Sherpas are renowned for their strength and courage. They practiced an old version of Tibetan Buddhism and are from the Bhotia - the Tibetan related ethnic groups inhabiting several high valleys in northeastern Nepal. Onward and upward, we trekked! I tried to camouflage my tension concerning the bridge crossing. I belted out, "The hills are alive with the sound of. . . .la-la-la-la," but couldn't remember the lyrics and settled back into my state of mindlessness.

I counted my steps as a diversion. We eventually arrived at the gorge, and I discovered the bridge was only a larger version of Sky Bridge, the swinging bridge I crossed as a kid in Gatlinburg, Tennessee. I felt a surge of power from within. This energy was working its way to the surface, manifesting in an ear-shattering cry – GERONIMO! I leaped onto the remaining slats while my voice reverberated around the fathomless gorge into eternity and back again. I shifted my weight from left to right, right to left, working up a swinging momentum that might have impressed a circus crowd of children, but Vittorio and Nawang were already one hundred yards further up and missed my reckless display.

We marched several hours more and then made camp on a lofty but level clearing. I sensed a certain comradeship with Edmund Hillary and Tenzing Norgay as we settled in for the night. After Nawang created a special supper of pickled lamb's tongue with a variety of dried grass, I reflected on the extraordinary feat we had accomplished - scaling and descending those sublime summits. I then drifted off to sleep with sugar plum fairies dancing in my head. We awoke at dawn and were greeted with steaming hot *chai* and rice porridge. Another day, another adventure, I took an extra deep breath, filled my lungs with pristine Himalayan atmosphere, and spent fifteen minutes doing my morning Sun Salutations. I was born double-jointed, which enabled me to excel at the most intricate and strenuous yoga positions, even impressing Swamis, Yogis and the like.

The terrain became somewhat unfriendly; however, the abundance of pines and oaks was soothing. And the melodic songs of the Spiny Babbler, a bird native only to Nepal, gave me an infusion of chirpiness and helped lift my spirits as well as my feet.

Actually, I found the descents a breeze. I guess it depends on your knees, and my 24-year-old knees had had minimum wear and tear. Vittorio endearingly called me his *capra di montagna* (mountain goat). I took it as a compliment.

Up until now, we had only crossed ankle-deep sleepy streams, but looming in front of us was a raging river with a speed that surpassed level six of whitewater rafting. I studied Nawang's facial expression to decipher the risk factor. The ruddy, weathered face of our Sherpa gave no hint of alarm. About fifty yards up the river, two men were waving their arms for us to come to them. From what I could gather from Nawang's preposition-free vocabulary, the two locals were professional river crossers. The onslaught of trekking tourism had created an abundance of never before thought of careers. Evidently, these river crossers were extra sure-footed and knew the exact underwater route. One brawny crosser signaled for Nawang to hop on, piggy-back style. The other guy motioned for Vittorio to mount, and they both crossed uneventfully.

My turn and I could foresee the problem of my lanky legs dragging in the water, becoming unwanted rudders that might throw the river-crosser off course. Vittorio was whistling for me to COME. He was not accustomed to my engaging quirks yet. I insisted I would pay double to have the duo cross me - one on each arm to keep me stabilized as we forged the current side by side. I'm glad I couldn't understand their response. They looked puzzled then smirked. The river was only knee-deep, but what a turbulent current. I lived to tell the story, slipped into my flip flops and carried on.

It was a mountain away where we would be pitching camp; however, Nawang had a luxurious surprise for us. He eventually led us to a small, wooden one-roomed house with an ample porch. The host of the house invited us to eat his `menu of the day' for a reasonable fee. We jubilantly staked our space on the porch. We then filled ourselves with succulent tidbits of rice and vegetables with other indescribable crunchy stuff. To my dismay, I later discovered the crunch was finely chopped chicken feet and petrified gizzards! At least that explained why I had a toenail wedged between my rear molars. Local homemade lassi (watered down yogurt with a pinch of sugar) made a delectable dessert.

Nawang and our host seemed to be best buddies, perhaps our Sherpa got a kickback from the bill, or maybe the guy was his brother. It looked like we were in store for another treat. We were invited to sleep inside the house with our chef and his entourage, consisting of nine people and at least four generations. The night was chilly due to the altitude, and there was a welcoming fire crackling inside. I voted for a cozy communal sleep, unaware that the great-great-grandma was going to chant the entire night.

She worked the mala beads through her gnarled but nimble fingers without pausing to breathe. Mala prayer beads were strung together from the Buddha Chitta plant's natural seeds, endemic to the region, and were a must for the Tibetan community members. Grandma's droning chant, plus a dozen hours of hiking, eventually led me into an abrupt, somewhat erratic sleep. The interruptions of a babe's piercing cry for milk, plus anatomical vibrations that rattled the windows, kept me from sinking into a night of delta sleep.

We awoke pre-sunrise with our roommates' buzzing activity, gulped our *chai* and porridge, and continued the journey up the yellow brick road. As we trudged skyward with anticipation, it was dually heart wrenching and admirable to watch young girls and women, weighted down with tons of wood, produce and water, merrily overtake us as we struggled uphill. Cheerfully they smiled as Nawang greeted them with "*Tashidelek*," conveying blessing, good luck and good health. They certainly needed it since women in Nepal faced systemic discrimination, particularly in rural areas; however, these females looked happy as larks. I guess Women's Empowerment activists hadn't reached them yet, so they were content with their lot.

2. KATHMANDU

Meanwhile, back to the heart of Kathmandu and hippie road, dubbed "Freak St." This was the epicenter of the hippie trail and true Nirvana, where shops and restaurants had popped up to cater to a Western taste. The hippies, spiritual seekers, and draft dodgers headed to Nepal to search for enlightenment and, above all, bargain-priced marijuana and hashish. These drugs were sold openly with the government's stamp of approval.

My favorite hangout was the Everest Snack Bar. Ram Gopal (better known as KC) started his first entrepreneurial success there. Bull's eye, his burgers, fast-food, cakes and pies were spot-on. He always had a patient line of followers waiting to get their toe inside.

Admittedly, I was an atypical hippie. I guess I looked the part and could talk the talk, but I was allergic to grass, hashish, hypnotics, magic mushrooms, speed, and hallucinogens. I tried everything on the market, without success, but most of my friends overlooked my affliction. My only addiction was to the enticing, mouth-watering, delectable dessert, BANANA SPLIT. I was good at spinning a story, more often embellished, and basically became an excellent ornament.

I was a staunch non-conformist and was doing the hippie trail in reverse, flying in from the East. The rest of the stragglers on Freak St. had undoubtedly arrived from the West in their trusty, German-made Volkswagen vans via Istanbul, Teheran, Herat, Kabul, Peshawar, Lahore, Delhi, and then northeast to Nepal. Whatever mode of travel we used to arrive at this Shangri-La valley of Kathmandu, we bonded instantaneously in our joint achievement of actually arriving there alive.

Another of my atypical hippie idiosyncrasies was my aversion to horoscopes, fortune cookies, fortune tellers, tarot cards, and the I-Ching. You see, I had a predisposition to subliminal suggestion and reacted to all the rare side effects of medications by only reading the prospectus, without even popping any pills. I didn't want to be programmed.

It had become an art to avoid having my astrology chart read. People asked me my zodiac sign, rather than my name, to make sure I would be compatible enough to exchange names with them. I was a double-Libra, and that was a perk since everyone seemed to get along with Libras.

Back to the Everest Snack Bar – it was there that travelers traded gems of transit info, and, as a matter of fact, it was there that I met Vittorio, and he invited me to the elephant camp. It was also where I first heard about the up-market eatery of the valley, the Yak and Yeti Restaurant. Co-owner and flamboyant hotelier and restaurateur, the celebrated Russian ballet dancer, Boris Lisanevich, was there in person to meet, greet and seat you.

Boris had danced in a Russian ballet troupe in Monte-Carlo, then danced his way around South America and headed east to dance in India. He eventually hung up his ballet shoes and opened the members-only "Club 300" in Calcutta, India, for a decade. There he met the King of Nepal, and they became friends.

This friendship eventually led to his partnership in Kathmandu's first proper hotel, The Royal Hotel. That posh hotel saw its halcyon days in the '50s and '60s, as Boris played a crucial role in paving the way for tourism in Nepal.

By 1969 the hotel had closed, but a large wing of the Palace was renovated to accommodate the now-famous Yak and Yeti Restaurant. Arriving only two years after the grand inauguration, this in-demand restaurant was high on my list of places to experience. It had become synonymous with Kathmandu.

I traveled alone by choice. I quickly discovered that I could create my tailor-made itinerary better without interference, and dually, I would be free to meet other explorers and switch my course at a moment's whim.

My preferred mode of exploring a new place was by bicycle. The same afternoon I checked into my spartan hotel, the Panoramic, I found a suitable beat-up bike to rent. Each morning I'd take an intoxicating pedal to the surrounding villages, always on alert for fascinating artifacts that I could re-sell and turn a neat profit. It also gave me time to do some soul-searching and reflect upon my extraordinary, round-about voyage to this lofty paradise.

* * *

Growing up in the land of milk and honey, in a somewhat antebellum, pampered lifestyle, gave me the false confidence that `all would be well.' My parents' Gold American Express card, hidden in my flat body pouch, obviously attributed to my happy-go-lucky attitude. I didn't plan on using it, but that card proved to be a reassuring safety net as I walked a tightrope into the unknown.

It all began with a mere suggestion. My friend Rise, a lovely Jewess from NYC, had finished her degree in Fine Arts with Honors at Columbia U in the Big Apple. However, her mother's sour reply was, "But, your brother is a doctor." So, Rise headed south to study medicine in my natal crescent city. We were like chalk and cheese but bonded by our mutual passion for rag-time jazz and French Quarter food, fun, and fashion. Her acclaimed paintings were on show in my mom's art gallery, where I often hung out and helped out.

My creative outlet was in the fashion field, and I even strut through a few unmemorable modeling advertisements on local TV. My discerning "nothing is impossible" pal Rise told me one sweaty hot afternoon at

Jackson Square, "Tyke, you should go to Paris and become a fashion model. New Orleans is too provincial for you." A seed was planted, and a star was born as my jumbled, but buoyant brain attempted to digest that possibility. I was twenty-three, footloose, and fancy-free with a cousin living in Paris. The wheels of my mind, lubricated with intentions of fame and fortune, started to spin out of control.

I escaped New Orleans on the Ides of March in 1971, heading to France to visit Fran, my academic cousin. She was studying for her master's degree in French at the Sorbonne in Paris while falling in love with a handsome young Yugoslavian. I had booked my return flight home for the end of May, allowing myself several months to discover Paris's *haute couture*, the Beatles `swinging London,' and the *dolce vita* of Rome. Little did I know that it would be three years until I'd return home to New Orleans, and only for a short visit.

Before I knew it, I was aboard a Delta flight to NYC, then on to Paris. I was singing the lyrics to "I love Paris in the Spring. . . ." as I descended the wobbling steps, located my luggage and cracked helmet hairdryer. I leaped into the bus leaving Orly Airport headed to Paris city-center. Hallelujah! I spotted Fran – she and her handsome Balkan boyfriend were discreetly waving at me. Her suitor cooed in fractured French, "*Les cousines viennent dans different paquets*" (cousins sure come in different packages). Wearing my Mary Quant mini dress with knee-high white boots, I felt like the cat's meow.

My cousin was the spitting image of Marilyn Monroe, while my lanky frame boasted the aristocratic, streamlined curves of Popeye's gal, Olive Oyl. Fran studied while I shopped. I had a pair of thigh-high kid leather brown boots made to measure on the famed Rue de Saint Honore - the perfect accessory for my hot pants and ankle long waistcoat.

If I was to become a noteworthy model, I knew that first impressions were vital. I packed my *haut couture* fashion favorites, a believable copy of a Pucci mini dress, my embroidered bell-bottom jeans & a tie-dye crop top, a smocked maxi-dress, and other trendy items.

After three weeks of inhaling everything Paris had to offer, I flew to London to stay with friends I had met in the Caribbean. WOW! London was swinging, and I was swaying. I was invited to the Cannes Film Festival and somehow ended up in Marseille. I unfolded my battered Rand McNally world map and discovered I was only a thumbnail away from Ibiza, the hippie enclave and dirt cheap paradise for creative hopefuls.

I reflected on my destiny; was it fate or perhaps intuition that led me to that idyllic isle in the sparkling Mediterranean - then catapulted me up to the lofty, ancient valley of Kathmandu? How could I have conceived that the sleepy little Spanish island, afloat in the Mediterranean Sea, would become a pivotal point in my global travels, as well as in my life?

It was there in Ibiza that a semi-venomous travel bug bit me. The isle was a Herculean stone's throw from the mainland of Spain, just west of Valencia. Kenny, a nefarious friend of a friend from New Orleans, brought me up to speed about this virtually unknown island. He described Ibiza as a jewel in the Med's crown, inhabited with a fascinating mix of worldwide drop-outs, infused with authentic writers, artists, and internationally titled.

There was also a growing band of elite American draft dodgers whose folks turned a blind eye while sponsoring their offspring's hideaway. Ibiza became a bona fide hippie haven that attracted the backpacker variety and the hippie-chic plus celebrities from all over Europe and beyond. The local *Ibicencos* were ultra tolerant to the influx of weirdos that jump-started their economy after many lean years of diminishing opportunities.

It was a balmy afternoon in Ibiza at the Montesol Café when a well-spoken Brit, Julian, announced he was off to Marrakesh and was looking for someone to split the *petrol*. After two seconds of reflection, I recklessly responded, "Hey, me!" and we sealed the deal over a cup of coffee. He was heading down to Morocco to meet his girlfriend Maria, a Portuguese beauty, and also buy carpets for resale.

My wanderlust dreams were birthed in Ibiza, but Morocco became the catalyst and springboard from which my extended travels would commence. Julian booked the night ferry from Ibiza to Barcelona. From there, we had a ten-hour drive down the zigzagging, picturesque eastern coastline of Spain.

Then we took the ferry to Morocco. Within five hours, we were in AFRICA! From that point, we had a spectacular full day's drive south along the western coast of Morocco to Mohammedia. We spent the night there with my extraordinary ex-roommates from New Orleans, and by noon the next day, we were in the fabled market town of MARRAKESH. . . VOILÀ! *Camels, veiled ladies, snake charmers, bazaars*! It was a mixture of Middle Eastern and African cultures. Is this for real?

My only reference point to such exotic unfamiliarity was on the silver screen. I had not been taught any protocol for a female tourist in Morocco. I arrived in this mystical land in hippie garb - wearing my hip-hugger jeans, short-sleeved t-shirt, and sporting colorfully streaked hair, flying in every direction.

Colin, the British hairdresser in Ibiza, had convinced me to let him tint my blond streaks with vivid colors. I agreed without persuasion. However, while shopping in Marrakesh's village markets, it became clear that the local children couldn't resist grabbing onto my long, electric-colored hair, pick up their feet, and swing. To avoid 30-pound bodies dislocating my neck, I stuffed my hair up under a scarf. Local women always covered their hair with dignity. I followed their example.

Now with Maria, the sultry, gorgeous, no-nonsense *Portuguesa*, who carried a lethal knife in her right boot, we headed south to Tan-Tan Desert to experience the bi-annual *Fantasia*. Maria knew the ropes and wore local attire with her head covered elegantly. I could understand how Julian fell head-over-heels for her. She had style.

Whoa, the traditional exhibition of horsemanship, a stylized reenactment of a desert Cavalry charge, was undoubtedly something leftover from "Lawrence of Arabia." At that precise moment, I vowed, "*I have one life and one planet – my QUEST is to discover both!*" I was in a glorious free-fall, not knowing exactly where I would be going or what I would be doing, but knowing my life would be radically transformed.

Shortly after that, I bumped into two American girls traveling with a young French aristocrat, who had a fake foot curiously enough. We clicked, and I hitched a ride with them to Casablanca. From Casablanca, I eventually flew to Rome for a month of WOW, then to the trendy Greek island of Mykonos, WOWEE, and on to Bangkok. From there, I trained and taxied through mesmerizing Malaysia to Singapore. I then flew to Bali, the utopian paradise highly recommended to me by my friends back in Ibiza. After a month of "You'd never believe it," I flew to Kathmandu. That was my venturous route of arriving, from the East to this infamous hippie-haven in Nepal.

* * *

Freak Street was a stone's throw to Durbar Square, the pulsating heart of fragrant Old Town Kathmandu - Nepal's capital. To the south were all the hippie type shops selling Nepalese accessories, while the hip local shopkeepers wore the latest fashion from the west – each craving the others' "look." Directly to the west were the ancient temples from the 11th century, and across the square to the east was the entrance to the former Royal Palace. Durbar means "palace" and is a crucial site for Buddhist and Hindu rituals, holy ceremonies, royal coronations, plus an optimal place to meet other transients.

It was there I met an unusually decent young man who asked me if I was new to Kathmandu; if so, he'd show me around. I pretended I was a Nepal novice and accepted his generous offer. Later I discovered he was a French doctor and a volunteer for *Médecins San Frontiéres*, doing his internship at the valley clinic.

He appeared to be a younger brother of Alain Delon, without the movie-star sparkle, but the same insolent expression that the French tend to wear. I guess he noticed my well-cut jeans and the famed, tie-dyed Lothar blouse from the French Riviera. My long hair was less frizzy in Nepal's dry climate, and I had it brushed to one side, exposing my dangling earring with Tibetan turquoise and coral stones.

Jean-Jacques and I bicycled in a single file to avoid hitting chickens, kids, water buffalo, poop, and ruts. Arriving at Kathmandu's northeastern side, namely Boudhanath, it was like rolling into `paradise lost.' He explained that the area was the closest we could get "culturally" to Tibet, with all roads closed to Lhasa, a few hundred miles away. Dominated by a massive white *Stupa* (Buddhist monument) that had become the matrix to that Tibetan community, the buzzing commerce revolved around it in haphazard harmony.

Being an informed guide, Jean-Jacques intently explained that the colorful neighborhood was a sacred Buddhist site and home to most Tibetan exiles in Kathmandu, who fled in the late 1950s, hot on the heels of the Dalai Lama. We circled the *stupa*, spinning the prayer wheels and ringing the bells devoutly. In fascinating detail, Jean-Jacques told me that prayer wheels must be rotated clockwise; the same direction the mantras were written and also the sun's movement across the sky. Each time the multi-hued flags rippled overhead, a mantra vibrated from its motion. It made perfect sense to me. Allowing the wheels and flags to do the praying was a lot less tedious than hours of the verbal method, "*Om mani padme hum.*"

Jean-Jacques, who I instantly dubbed J-J, went on to say that at the core of each prayer wheel is a "life tree" made of wood or metal, with specific mantras written on them. The significance of Boudhanath, above all else, was how it symbolized freedom for the Tibetan exiles. There they practiced their faith without any fear of resistance and thrived in their shops and restaurants.

My French was vague, but J-J's accented English was excellent, and I understood every word. Nevertheless, he sandwiched, "Tu comprends?" in between every slice of information. I nodded with enthusiasm or replied politely, "*Oui monsieur*." I enjoyed my lengthy tour, but my hypoglycemic symptoms started kicking in, and I blurted out, "*J'ai faim*," pointing to my concave stomach. I would have been happy with some *chexo*, a cheap Tibetan rice and yogurt dish, but J-J insisted we dine at the Yak and Yeti Restaurant. "Bingo," I replied eagerly, "*Oui oui, j'amerais bien*."

* * *

I felt like Cinderella with her prince charming as we entered the impressive dining area in a converted wing of the Palace, Lal Durbar. J-J was obviously a regular. We were greeted by the owner, Boris, "*Bienvenue Docteur*, your usual table for two?"

Boris appeared to be an aging boxer rather than an ex-Russian ballet dancer. His once-upon-a-time magnificent muscles were now padded and sagging, and his square face drooped with jowls, but the sparkle in his eyes and his warm Ukrainian smile made me feel like a bona fide VIP. The men, who didn't extend their hand, gave a nod of recognition to my escort as Boris ushered us to the "usual table for two." I wondered who the other person usually was.

The men made eye contact with me, but the ladies kept their gaze lowered and I felt pelted with whispers. Perhaps it was an untimely debut for me to be presented to the high society of that tight-knit clique. I was clearly the youngest female in that hallowed hall, and I suspect I was looked upon as a trespasser.

J-J explained there was a sizeable foreign ex-pat population in the valley due to the many embassies within that quaint kingdom. The representations of embassies included France, Germany, Russia, Egypt, Australia, and the US. These multinationals not only felt like the foreign elite of this lush valley - they were. Apart from the diplomatic corps and its staff members, the remaining tables were filled with a sprinkling of imported doctors, dentists, developers & well-heeled travelers.

I loved to eat the local fare but couldn't locate a single Nepalese or Tibetan dish on the oversized menu, so I decided on borsch. I noticed that the elite clientele was slurping bright red beetroot soup as we made our royal entrance. When invited to dine, I always chose the cheapest entrée to avoid any commitment or obligation. The borsch was filled with other tasty vegetables and huge sour cream dollops, accompanied by hot, homemade bread!

However, a bi-product from the impacting calorie-rush sent me into a limp, digestive stupor. I had to stay focused and concentrate as J-J quizzed me on rag-time jazz when I admitted I was from New Orleans. My curly dark hair, somewhat straightened by the sheer weight, plus my X-L lips and dark tan, usually led people to believe I was a mix. Of what?

When in NYC, I was a Jewess, while in Rome, I was Italian, when in France, I became North African. I decided it was great to have a versatile `air' rather than appearing to be a stereotype American. I even sewed Canadian maple leaves to my jacket since there was so much controversy about the war in Vietnam and US involvement.

During coffee, Nigel, from the British Embassy, slapped J-J on the shoulder and pulled up a chair to join us. Nigel was blond, quite fair, and very friendly. He was far from being a hippie; however, he was a seeker. J-J and Nigel agreed that science has shown that when people come to-gether to meditate and pray, electromagnetic fields shift, violence reduces, healing occurs, and peace prevails. J-J, finishing his hands-on qualification as a medical doctor, was fully aware that prayer had a posi-tive effect on healing, therefore bonding him with Nigel on many levels.

Having spent many years in Kathmandu, Nigel was a regular at the local Tibetan monastery, but his latest passion was studying Gestalt Therapy. He explained that the therapists don't aim to change their clients. Their role is to help them develop their self-awareness and how they are in the present moment, thus enabling them to rectify issues affecting their lives. I intently nodded in agreement and curiously asked Nigel if he had developed self-awareness yet and if so, was it improving his life. I was always up-front and interested in new methods of self-improvement. Nigel laughed and admitted, "It's a process."

After all, Libras are always doing a balancing act; tolerant, all-encompassing, people-pleasers seeking harmony. I was a double Libra - perhaps that's why I was still eager to learn a new teaching, a radical philosophy, or another religion. I wanted to be able to resonate with everyone, no matter how distinct they were. After all, God created us all equal and loves us all. At least my God does.

J-J, gentleman that he was, led me back to the Panoramic Hotel, then he pedaled away into the starry night. Nigel said he'd pick us up the following day to visit the Monkey Temple, but J-J bowed out since he had a twelve-hour work shift, saving lives, comforting the bereaved, and treating the ill. However, he put a good word in for Nigel, explaining that he was a fascinating, down-to-earth guy, considering his noble background.

* * *

I was outside at 10 am when Nigel pulled up in his Peugeot sedan, a rare sight in the valley - there were only a handful of cars since bicycles and rickshaws were the accepted, non-polluting mode of travel. Swayambhu Temple (monkey hill) was our destination, atop a glorious hill, two miles west of Kathmandu city. These primates chose one of the planet's most awe-inspiring religious sites. Did they know something we didn't?

The monkeys drew pilgrims and tourists to this spot from every corner of the world. It is said to be one of the holiest Buddhist religious temples of the country since the 5th century and probably one of the most sacred among Buddhist pilgrimage sites for Tibetans as well as Hindus.

The *stupa* had Buddha's eyes and eyebrows painted onto it - almost graffiti style. I was breathless and sweating as we struggled up the last ten steps and practically fell upon the gigantic thunderbolt scepter. The mega thunderbolt symbolized reality's nature, indicating endless creativity, potency, and skillful activity.

The fact that Tibetan monks, Brahmin Hindu priests, and Newar nuns lived on-site in unison gave visitors motivation to explore this intriguing temple. However, the free-range holy monkeys inhabiting the site were possibly the biggest draw.

Since I was a teen, I had an affinity with primates. I mothered a spider monkey named Tyrone, who swung from the rustic exposed rafters of our country home, not far from New Orleans. Tyrone warmed my baby Easter chicks by gathering them together in his long-armed embrace. However, the temple monkeys, holy or not, were downright fierce.

Having read there was a threat of zoonotic transmission of infectious agents at monkey temples, especially with this variety of Mucaca Mulatta monkeys, I was on alert. Upon that spooky contemplation, one critter leaped on my head, poking its sticky fingers into my left eye, and snatched a candy bar from my shirt pocket. That blatant little thief had the audacity not only to ruffle my aura and block my chakra points but also to threaten my plunging blood sugar.

A twenty-minute walk led us to a shady monkey-less patch where we could sit in lotus positions and exchange our self-awareness conclusions. I jumped at every chance to advance my spiritual growth. However, enlightenment remained elusive thus far. I listened intently to Nigel expound on Gestalt psychology of perception. I stored some mental notes.

I wondered if EST (Erhard Seminars Training) was parallel teaching. EST was also part of the Human Potential Movement and was a form of Large Group Awareness Training, in which the goal was psychological growth. Too many hours were spent in large groups, deprived of food and water, and badgered by stewards. The fasting portion put me off, but the psychological growth part was mind-blowing. My conclusion: if it wasn't helpful, it wasn't harmful, and I met some interesting people.

Nigel said his years of studying Buddhism had given him a sturdy base upon which to build. He insisted that next on the list was a visit to the Kopan Monastery. Not to spoil his enthusiasm, I didn't mention I had already checked it out, and besides, I still had a lot more to learn about Buddhism. Accompanied by unreserved body language, Nigel mimed how the monks chanted sacred texts, usually followed by a cacophony of crashing cymbals, thumping drums, and blaring Tibetan horns.

He then demonstrated "throat singing," a skill in which Tibetan monks excel. Their unique form of throat chanting produces multiple distinct pitches simultaneously. This skill helps them focus their concentration, transcending thought itself. I realized it was certainly worth a shot and definitely a step up in drama from the Methodist Church I faithfully attended until I became a counter-culture activist.

I had an appointment to get my ears pierced that afternoon, so I suggested we visit the monastery the following day. I wanted some meaningful souvenirs from Nepal and decided that having my ears pierced along the entire rim of cartilage would be a flashy choice. The Nepalese women were so elegant with their slender figures draped in saris and their piercings and face decorations enhanced by their enormous, Khol-rimmed eyes.

The central street pharmacy had a dirt floor, and spider webs were suspended in the shop's corners and spun across the upper shelves. I had purchased ten tiny gold hoops as advised by a fellow traveler since gold was usually non-allergic. The female pharmacist rolled her eyes when she saw me, took out a weathered box with a scary needle while I sat on a child's stool so she could reach my left ear.

I had not considered how tough cartilage could be and started singing to block out her huffing and puffing and the popping noise of the needle breaking through the tough collagen fibers. I told the nice lady I would take a rain check for the other ear. I hoped the piercing hadn't interfered with my meridian points and that my body would reroute and restore any energy loss. I would harmonize my chakras when I got back to the hotel.

How exciting, I would be the very first in my group of friends and acquaintances to sport such exotic ear décor. In 1971, only gypsies and "ladies of the night" pierced their ears in my neck of the woods. My next souvenir would be a tattoo. Almost all the local ladies of Nepal had a delicate, indelible ink design on their flawless copper skin - so why shouldn't I?

3. BUDDHIST MONASTERY

I awoke the following morning with anticipation and headed off with Nigel and Jean-Jacques to the monastery, situated on a lofty hill overlooking the valley. We were welcomed by a huge sign – Temple Rules – "Don't take your shoes off, don't point and be sure to greet Buddha, keep your head down. *Namaste* is a Hindu greeting, not Buddhist, so don't use it."

Once past that warm welcome, we wove our way into the monastery. Our ten-hour visit turned out to be a crash course on Buddhism, and I congratulated myself for taking legible notes so I could study them and apply those truths to my life. I was stunned to discover that Buddha was not the name of a deity or even a great teacher. Buddha literally meant "the enlightened one." Siddhartha Gautama was called Buddha – he was a philosopher, spiritual teacher, and religious leader born in Lumbini, Nepal. Why did this Indian prince leave behind a life of luxury to become a wandering holy man, and how did he become an enlightened being? He made such an impact that he is still revered as the founder of the world religion of Buddhism. Such a widespread belief does not speak of a god or a higher power; however, supernatural beings are prominent in Tibetan Buddhism.

I learned that I didn't necessarily need external stimulants to satisfy the feeling of excessive outward stimuli. Instead, I needed to focus on making the internal enough by slowing down and fully engaging in the present moment. Our attachment to anything that makes us feel good ultimately makes us less happy in the long run. (I had my doubts with that theory.)

I was very familiar with the concept of karma – since I was told from childhood, what you sow, you will also reap. That boomerang effect helped keep me somewhat in line. Compassion is the hallmark of Buddhism, and its goal is Nirvana – a state of liberation and freedom from suffering. I was convinced that this religion would fit into my lifestyle as well as my slightly self-focused goals. For the next weeks, I reviewed my notes on the basic teachings of Buddha.

The Three Universal Truths
Nothing is lost in the universe
Everything changes
The laws of cause and effect

The Three Training Practices
Ethics - The golden rule
Meditation - Developing one's mind
Wisdom – Discernment, enlightenment

The Four Noble Truths
The truth of suffering
The truth of the cause of suffering - due to attachment
The truth of the end of suffering - it ceases with final liberation
The truth of the path that leads to the end of suffering – final liberation, Nirvana

The Five Noble Precepts
Do not kill
Do not steal
Do not lie
Do not misuse sex
Do not get intoxicated

These precepts will develop mind and character to make progress on the path to enlightenment. The bottom line is, Buddhists believe in a cycle of death and rebirth called *samsara*. Not to be confused with reincarnation, Buddhists believe in the mind-stream: a continuous existence in one of the six realms. Through karma and eventual enlightenment, they hope to escape *samsara* and achieve nirvana - an end to all suffering as they leave the cycle of life, death, and rebirth. Amen.

I could fully embrace this belief system, except I could not get my head around the idea that there was not a single reference to a higher power. How can there not be a God? How did everything come into being? How can something come from nothing? I desperately wanted to sit down with Siddhartha and have a cozy tête-à-tête.

Yes, I realized that there were missing pieces to this Buddhism puzzle, but I was happy to glean what I thought was acceptable and toss the rest. The *oms* and mantras were definitely working for me, and I was raised on the karma concept - the golden rule. The five Noble Precepts were simply a shortlist of the Ten Commandments. But best of all, it was a cool, counter-culture religion to have. It seemed genuine, and the adherents were devout – unlike the hypocritical, once a week dress parade I experienced in my youth.

Living smack dab in the middle of the Bible-belt of the USA, there were tons of ranting, raving radio evangelists who were frequently hauled off to jail for tax evasion or worse. The Christians I knew were very narrow-minded, judgmental, prudish hypocrites, except for my girlfriend, Beth. She was the real deal, a teen Mother Teresa, a genuine do-gooder who kept me on track. However, she moved to Houston when we were fourteen.

I was intrigued by the person of Jesus, who always had to set straight the self-righteous religious leaders. He certainly embodied perfect love and was a true example to follow. I secretly added Jesus to my eclectic collage of heroes and considered him a truly good man and a prophet to be looked up to. His teachings, along with those of Siddhartha, made an appealing mix.

After many months of hanging out on pristine beaches, gazing at stunning mountains, dining with romantic views in Paris, London, Rome, Athens, Bangkok, Bali, and Kathmandu, I realized that even pleasure and beauty could become exhausted unless there is SOMETHING MORE. Mahesh, the orphaned Nepalese boy, became my mission focus in Kathmandu.

* * *

Ying Yang Restaurant on Freak St. had recently become one of the anchors of the budget-tourist district and a favorite for hippies, as well as locals. Along with his Spanish friend, Vidhya Shrestha created a space with offbeat décor that included an extensive sound system. The desire for Western music was paramount. As a matter of fact, anything from the West was in demand – particularly Levis blue jeans.

Vidhya concluded that the beard and sandal crowd had a bad name in his hometown, but he defended many writers, philosophers, artists, and generally good people. Inspired by his father, who opened the first orphanage in Kathmandu, Vidhya went out of his way to help the poor children. On his weekly "fast" day, when the restaurant was closed, he produced a `banquet' for the street kids, and they lined up for their share.

It was there that I met Mahesh, my adopted Nepali five-year-old boy. I call it `love at first sight.' He was patiently waiting in line as I walked by, then our eyes met and locked. I bent down to ask him his name, and he slipped his hand into mine. My heart melted, and I knew this would be an ongoing relationship.

I asked Vidhya to explain to Mahesh that I wanted to invite him to lunch every day and any evening he wanted. For a few rupees, you could enjoy a massive plate of rice and *dahl* (lentils) or buffalo meat-filled dumplings known as *momos*. Brownies were everyone's favorite dessert on Freak St. and undoubtedly the best, this side of my grandma's kitchen. Appearing to be a full-fledged hippie, I had to specify that I wanted a plain brownie, or else someone would sell me one chock-full of hashish. After all, it was a legal, dirt-cheap drug.

As an alternative dessert, I talked Vidhya into adding "banana split" to his menu. Bananas were accessible since they were grown in the Chitwan Forest. Three scoops of ice cream, chocolate sauce, and a few chopped nuts, voilà - whipped cream was optional. Flocks of semi-resident American hippies added the delectable dessert to their daily intake. I even convinced the owner to make yogurt ice cream for a healthy choice.

Not to sound too philanthropic, many of the street kids were adopted by the travelers passing through Kathmandu, so the children were accustomed to rotating aunts and uncles. However, I never came to terms with leaving sweet Mahesh, and I ache for him this very day. I formed part of the "me" generation - the post-war spoiled brats, who grew up in the land of plenty and still wanted more. The self-awareness quest might appear very selfish, but I soothed my conscience with dreams of Nirvana. Come to think of it, the most profound joy I had in that magical valley was probably my time spent with Mahesh, focused on meeting his needs.

I was presently facing a colossal disappointment and a real trial. My favorite blue jeans were gone. My lodging, The Panorama Hotel, had been my 'home sweet home' for more than a month. The Nepalese owner Tuladhar – known as "Dad," lowered his eyes as he confessed, "Mum, the jeans you left with me at the desk for washing are gone - destroyed."

This news came as a tragic shock since I only had two pairs of jeans, and they were the ones with soul. They flaunted hand-embroidered designs from all my favorite places. My eyes were ablaze as I pleaded with him, "You're kidding me, aren't you?" "No, mum, it was the cycle, mum." Exasperatedly, I raised my voice, "Why did you use such a fast cycle? Can't you adjust your washing machine?" Dad replied calmly, "Not that cycle, mum, the bi-cycle."

"What bicycle?" I fumed. "The bicycle of my washing boy when he was hauling clothes to the river to stone-wash them. Your trousers got tangled in the bi-cycle chain, mum. Full of holes, mum." I often wondered if that was a fib, and "Dad" actually sold my jeans on the black market - embroidered jeans would reap a small fortune, in rupees anyway.

Realizing that screaming or crying would not bring my jeans back, I wondered if it was perhaps my karma. Yes, I had to admit to myself; maybe I deserved this misfortune after all. I took a deep breath, "*Om mani padme hum,*" refocused and smiled.

However, I was sad to think about leaving Kathmandu, my newly made friends, the beauty of the majestic mountains, the refreshing, dry air, the colorful Tibetans with their fascinating culture, the buzz of Freak Street, the temples and villages, really EVERYTHING! I vowed to return, but knowing there were still more people, places, and belief systems to discover, I carried on with my original plan.

My strategy, since the onset of my journey eastward, was to arrive in Goa, India, for Christmas. When our friends in Ibiza saw us off on the ferry that bright sunny morning, connected by rolls of unraveling toilet paper, as we drifted out to sea en route to Morocco, we shouted back and forth, "See you in Goa in December, don't forget!" Unlike the Canary Islands, Ibiza enjoyed only seasonal tourism due to the damp, cold winters. A large part of the hippie population migrated to the south of India to enjoy tropical winters and give-away priced drugs. Goa was a favorite among the Ibiza crowd.

Vittorio had arrived back from an extended hike up to the base camp of Mount Everest. I think he realized I might have been a handicap to his peace and pace. Anyway, I could invite him along with J-J and Nigel to the Ying Yang Restaurant for a farewell soiree and introduce them to Vidhya and Mahesh, along with the fascinating assortment that hung out there.

It was a memorable evening, and no one seemed to mind me singing and dancing atop the sturdy go-go table. I wore my rainbow-colored Tibetan tunic over my black Moroccan trousers, and a huge chunk of turquoise swung around my neck on a single strip of leather. Even though I didn't indulge in alcohol or drugs, the exhaled 'weed' from dozens of smokers was enough to whack me out.

We exchanged addresses, promising to stay in touch as I handed out cards from my mother's art gallery in the French Quarter. I never carried a camera but was grateful for the photos Vittorio mailed me, especially the one of Mahesh.

I insisted on seeing the world through my almond-shaped hazel eyes, rather than the camera's limiting lens. I had friends with comfy couches in Paris, London, and Rome, so I didn't need a home. The rest of the time, I would be on exotic travels where dollar-a-night hotels provided a place to lay my head and dream of my next adventure.

* * *

While boarding Air India's night flight, heading to Agra, I conjured up images of the splendid Taj Mahal. That marble palace was undoubtedly the seventh wonder of the world and certainly the best example of Mughal architecture, displaying the illustrious past of India's presently poverty-stricken majority.

It was quite complicated to coordinate my flight with the full moon. Still, I knew the reflection of the lunar beams ricocheting off that entire marble surface would be illuminating to my body, mind, and spirit. I was dressed in white from head to toe, prepared to absorb the beams.

Looking around for a window seat to drink in the spectacular light display, I spotted only one available seat, and it happened to be next to Ali Baba. I grappled with stuffing my huge handbag into the overhead compartment while the tall, turbaned gentleman stood up and offered his help. "Uh, thank you so much; how fortunate that you speak English." He smiled, and his head bobbed from left to right in usual Indian fashion.

In Europe, I discovered that Americans have a free-ticket to intrude. However, I had a genuine desire to know what made people tick and asked questions out of pure interest. I decided on a mundane opener, "I guess you're going to see the Taj Mahal also?" He smiled again, revealing perfectly aligned white teeth, and replied that he was going to Agra on business.

I told him I was a "Seeker" and interested in different countries and cultures. His question stunned me, "What is your purpose in life?" Whoa, I planned on an hour and a half of small-talk, but he was evidently up for a more in-depth exchange. I didn't have an answer up my sleeve, so I put the ball back into his court. "I noticed you're wearing a turban. Is that an accessory, or does it have a deeper meaning?" Well, that retort provoked a hardy laugh, and he said, "No, mum, I am a Sikh." I thought to myself, how apropos, a Seeker meets a Sikh. Serendipity?

Ah yes, when I was having high tea at the renowned colonial Hotel Raffles in Singapore with my Chinese girlfriend Na Lin, two tall, tur-baned doormen towered over most guests. I asked Na Lin, "What's their story? They certainly aren't locals."

She explained that they were Sikhs from Punjab, India, and due to their striking stature, hotels and restaurants often hired them as greeters. Na Lin also explained that their religion required them never to cut their hair, so they kept their locks tucked up under turbans. Also, the turbans and beards identified them as Sikhs, of which they were very proud. Now I knew enough to formulate an intelligent comment.

"Oh yes, I've heard that Sikhs never cut their hair, so it must save a lot of time and money not having to go to a barber. I guess you've heard about Samson the Nazarene, he was also forbidden to cut his hair, and when Delilah craftily had it shorn, all hell broke loose." I had been stalling for time to reply to Mr. Sikh's big question but finally formulated the right words and replied, "Actually, I am a seeker, and my purpose in life is to discover the Truth." Eureka, those were the magic words that sparked Mr. Sikh's evangelistic zeal. He replied eagerly, "Well, it is a good thing you sat here, young lady because I know the Truth." I nodded, "Intuition, I guess."

Mr. Sikh introduced himself as Mandeep Singh, so I politely replied with *"Namaste"* and lowered my head with respect and said, "I'm Marie France." Mandeep's eyes deepened with intensity and he confessed that all Sikhs were proud of their beliefs and wanted to be identified as Sikhs by their outward appearance.

He said, "Sikh gurus opposed the rigid Hindu caste system, wanting to bring unity amongst believers by giving them the same surnames and appearance." He continued, "At the end of the 15th century, Guru Nanar had a revelation that there was only one God, and equality among people was of utmost importance. The sacred book, Granth Sahib, finally replaced a series of Gurus. This formless, genderless, universal God encompasses all of reality, and no idols or symbols represent God."

Mandeep enthusiastically went on to say, "There is no status difference between men and women. Women fight alongside men and are also reigning leaders." I thought to myself, so far, so good, one God and women's rights. I pondered that concept; it just might be the truth or an essential slice of it. Inwardly I rehashed his ideology and faith. He believed there was no heaven or hell, contrary to Christian belief. Hell was considered life on earth. The goal was to merge your soul back into God's soul, breaking free from the cycle of rebirth by letting go of your ego. It sounded a bit like our Methodist preacher giving a sermon on 'dying to self.'

He continued, "There is no caste system, but instead, unified identity was the goal, tied together into one family, with one name, defender of the weak and always promoting justice. All men ideally have the same surname, Singh (lion), and all women Kaur (princess). Of utmost interest, all paths lead to one God! Therefore the God of Judaism, Islam, Buddhism, Hinduism, Jainism, Sikhism, and Christianity was the same. God is God."

I felt complimented that Mr. Singh considered me worthy of being taught about his religion. Or perhaps, like the Hari Krishnas, he would receive a gold star if he converted me to Sikhism. He made some excellent points, though.

A voice boomed over the loudspeaker, "Ladies and Gentlemen, we will not be landing in Agra due to the war going on between India and Pakistan. The Taj Mahal has been covered to protect it from becoming a target, and there are no landing lights on the airfield, so we will be proceeding on to New Delhi."

What? My world was coming apart at the seams. Why did I leave Nepal? My mind was trying to form a Plan B, but my emotions were stuck on Plan A. I looked over at Mr. Singh for a reaction. He had just solved "man's existence," so maybe he could do something about this disaster. He did not react, "Hey, aren't you upset about what the pilot said?" "Not really," responded Mandeep, "It sounds to me like a wise decision." My world had revolved around seeing that marble monument during the full moon. I took some deep breaths and tried to count my blessings while repeating my favorite mantra until we landed in New Delhi. "*Om mani padme hum, om mani padme hum. . . .*"

4. NEW DELHI, INDIA

It was 9 pm, and I still needed to find a place to sleep. I went to the hotel desk at the airport and quizzed the disinterested clerk about suitable lodgings. I wanted a centrally located modest hotel with at least a toilet and hand basin in the room. The agent scanned three pages before coming up with the Narula Hotel. I meditated for a minute and agreed.

I was not prepared for the traumatic trip to the taxi zone. At least twenty kids, teens and adults followed me. The kids clung to my legs as I dragged them along slowly, pulling up my trousers at intervals. The others tried to out-scream one another to get my attention for their car service and sleeping solution. I hadn't seen such chaos since last year's Mardi Gras, back in New Orleans.

What an assault on my senses! The noise, the pollution, the smells, the heat, and humidity were more than I could handle. I fought to extract my baggage from the grip of overzealous porters who wanted to deposit me into one of their private cars. I remained optimistic. Things could only get better. You can't make a judgment on a first impression. I remembered an expression Abraham Lincoln coined, "The only way to eliminate your adversary is to make them your friend." I was determined to make New Delhi my friend at all costs.

The Narula Hotel was not a disappointment. It looked as drab and uninviting as it did on the brochure, but the price fit my budget. The sheets looked worn but white, and the naked bulb that dangled from the ceiling gave off enough light for me to jot down all of that life-changing data Mr. Singh had downloaded to me during the flight. I was amazed at how pitch black it was outside.

I awoke several times abruptly in the night with a crashing sound outside, and when I arose the next morning, it was still pitch black. On closer inspection, I discovered that someone had blacked out the windows with tar paper. I couldn't even open the windows; perhaps they were waiting for new glass to be fitted.

Down at reception, they informed me that the hotel was ordered to obey the black-out regulations. Being the nation's capital and political headquarters, New Delhi was a prime target in the Indo-Pakistan War. Since the government ordered traffic lights switched off at night, vehicles were continually smashing into each other. Sadly enough, at the end of the thirteen-day war, it was estimated that there were more fatalities due to motor mishaps than actual fighting. I filled my days with sightseeing and not once had an inkling that a war was raging less than a thousand miles away. Due to the Pakistani General's strategic blunders, poor leadership, and weak military strategies, India emerged the victor, resulting in Bangladesh's birth.

Celebrating with the rest of the merrymakers, I danced in the streets 'til dawn, amid a cloud of colored powder, chanting, vic-tor-y, vic-tor-y! Some celebrators were tooting horns and others setting off firecrackers, dogs were howling, and babies were crying. It was a barrel of fun and utter pandemonium. I adored being an integral part of the celebration.

It just dawned on me why my mother advised me upon departure at the Moisant Field Airport, "Honey, remember to buy the Herald Tribune once in a while so that you can be up-to-date about wars, revolutions, or uprisings. It's best to avoid those areas, no matter how intriguing they seem to be."

My mother was a seasoned traveler and fearless. She was petite and slight but had a sumo wrestler's stamina and considered travel an equivalent to postgraduate studies. Mom was aware that I needed a Master's degree in *life* before settling down. She was also a shrewd businesswoman and willing to invest $50 a month in my extended travels, not wanting to interfere with my budding entrepreneurial skills. She was sure I had inherited lucrative genes from her "Spencer" side of the family.

It was the 16th of December and my rendezvous in Goa for Christmas was only a week away, so I decided to escape the following morning by train. I looked forward to the scenic journey to Bombay and then proceeding southward to the ex-Portuguese province of Goa. I discovered that being a jean-clad American traveler in India was, for once, preferable to being a posh British tourist. There was some remaining anti-colonial sentiment still alive, even after the death of British rule in 1947. India had slowly taken hold of its future during the past twenty-four years, and Mahatma Gandhi's life and death had not been in vain.

I was pleased that I had developed a meaningful relationship with Delhi and didn't let my initial impression steer me off course. The city was a proper mix of imperial splendor and backstreet squalor. Nevertheless, I gleefully envisioned the pomp and ceremony at Coronation Park in 1877. Queen Victoria arrived atop a spruced up elephant, amidst a sea of humanity, and she was duly proclaimed the Empress of India. Similarly, King Edward VII in 1903 and finally King George V, with his consort Queen Mary, in 1911, was subjected to the same ostentatious ceremony. It was there that King George V announced the transfer of the Capital of British India from Calcutta to New Delhi.

I suppose it was a bitter-sweet announcement for the locals, who had been under the Imperial thumb for more than half a century. British architects designed the new capital during the 1920s and 1930s, and the grand inauguration was in 1931. Meanwhile, Mahatma Gandhi was leading a peaceful civil-rights movement. His dress became simplistic and he most often appeared nearly nude, sporting a white loincloth with a white shawl over his deep brown, rail-thin shoulders. His fashion statement acknowledged the fact that the Indian poor were still naked because of Britain.

At the end of eight days of scrutinizing New Delhi, I qualified as a tourist guide, rickshaw driver, postal clerk, and museum curator. Perhaps I was even overqualified. I was a museum-aholic, drinking in the National Gandhi Museum, Nehru Memorial Museum, and the Gallery of Modern Art. I even bought a small fold-up chair that I could tote to the galleries, so I could loll around and take my time. Not to forget the twenty-odd temples I visited while contemplating my recent teachings about Hinduism and Buddhism.

The locals were kind and polite. However, their naïve inquisitiveness could easily have been mistaken for blatant intrusion. India was just too populated for privacy etiquette. As an American, I could relate to that endearing trait of prying.

The front desk of my hotel became my source of information. When I asked about out-of-the-way curio shops, the receptionist promptly introduced me to Arjun, most probably a relative. I must say, my favorite pastime was scouring the street markets and small shops for valuable-looking ethnic treasures that I could re-sell in the West to fund future travels.

Arjun was an eighteen-year-old, street-smart driver and guide, who turned out to be a gold-mine on wheels. He had a three-wheeler auto-rickshaw that he maneuvered with the skills of a Formula 1 race driver. He could even psyche out the sacred cows that wandered through the busy streets, oblivious to the life-threatening traffic. These carefree beasts might be someone's reincarnated grandmother, so they obviously had the right-of-way.

I hired Arjun "by the day" and was aware that he most probably skimmed a profit off the top of my purchases, but decided it was worth it not to be swamped by waves of taxi hopefuls each morning I stepped out of my hotel door. Mr. Patel, the receptionist, agreed to store my suitcases. My bags were crammed with Indian and Tibetan treasures, and I was relieved to travel south with only a tote bag.

The train was leaving for Bombay at 9 am sharp, and Arjun sped me to the station on time. Endowed with a gentle, kind personality, he insisted on accompanying me to the gate. I smiled, thanked him, and politely refused. I had managed on my own very well so far and reminded him that I'd be back in a month or so and we would reconnect. Arjun insisted on leading me to my platform for Bombay, so I gave in and gave him my hand. As we entered the station, I gripped Arjun's hand and shuddered to think that I had actually believed I could find the track by myself. There was an entire metropolis bustling inside the station. According to the 1970 census for New Delhi, the population hovered at 3,500,000 people. Well, every single inhabitant of the city was taking a train somewhere that morning. Arjun pulled me along to a ticket office, forcefully clearing a path with his free arm. He was even shouting at people to get out of the way. This shy young man had transformed into my hero. I thanked my higher power for blessing me in such an awesome way. As I boarded the train, I slipped Arjun a $10 note, the equivalent price of my train ticket in rupees. He stood there on the platform and waved to me until I disappeared out of sight. I never doubted that he was an angel.

* * *

I was forever indebted to the backpacker who told me to splurge on a CC train ticket. CC referred to an air-conditioned chair car and was cheaper than the sleep cars, but a considerable step up from economy fare. There was often standing room only, with people dangling out of windows and balancing on narrow connecting platforms between cars. The Indian-produced electric trains were said to be a jewel in the Indian Crown. I was impressed with the pollution-free invention that was thriving in this sub-continent. The West was filled with contamination from the diesel-fueled trains and needed techno tutoring from the Indians.

Having twenty-four hours and a mere thousand miles of rail before reaching Bombay, I looked forward to meditating, chanting, breathing exercises, reflecting on life, and enjoying the scenery. However, the be-spectacled Indian gentleman next to me had other plans. Without blinking an eye, he asked me, "Are you a man with long hair or a lady with no bosom." I laughed and admitted, "Option B." I understood his dilemma. I was five foot nine with broad shoulders and narrow hips. As far as he was concerned, my faded jeans, t-shirt and embroidered vest were men's clothing. I guess most of the ladies he knew had narrow shoulders, wide hips, ample busts, and wore a sari.

I was happy to be an atypical girl. Indians are charmingly truthful, without a filter of social etiquette, as we know it. Questions delivered in that sing-song accent didn't seem so invasive. He fired out the next query without a pause, "Where are you coming from, and why do you come to India, mum?" I smiled and replied, "I'm from the United States, and I'm here on a spiritual journey."

He squinted, adjusting his glasses, and replied, "Are you not happy with your religion, mum?" I answered with sincerity, "I was born into a somewhat Christian home, but that doesn't make Christianity the Truth. I need to study and experience other spiritualities."

His eyes widened, and he asked me if I had ever heard of Mahatma Gandhi. I grinned and said, "Of course, everyone's heard of Mahatma Gandhi." "Well, did you know that he almost became a follower of Je-sus?" "No, I had no idea."

"Oh yes, mum, he was a practicing Hindu when he read the gospels in your Holy Scriptures, and Gandhi was very impressed with the person and full message of Jesus, so he went to a church in Calcutta. However, they refused him because of the color of his skin and his caste. The smug elders told him only high-caste Indians and whites were allowed into the church.

Because of that rejection, he turned his back on Christianity." I was horrified, and I wanted to apologize for such blatant, racist treatment. He then laughed and said, "You must have heard the famous quote from

Gandhi, `*If it weren't for Christians, I'd be a Christian.*'" I thought to my-self; yep, Mahatma Gandhi hit the nail on the head. Christians are clearly what's wrong with Christianity.

Pausing a moment, I asked my rail-mate if he believed in Jesus. He rolled his eyes and said, "Of course! You see, in a sense, we Hindus don't consider Jesus as a Christian." (Jesus didn't either since the term wasn't used during his lifetime.) He went on to explain in the Hindu perspective, church or temple membership or belief is not as significant as a spiritual practice. In Sanskrit it is called *sadhana*. Since there is no Church of Hinduism, everyone holds their own spiritual and philosophical opinions. Then he explained, "In India, it is more common to ask, what is your *sadhana* (practice), rather than, what do you believe?"

He went on to clarify, "So when we are asked how we can see spirituality in our fellow Hindus, the answer is: by behavior and practice. We can ask ourselves if we are humble, are we tolerant, and are we compassionate. Are we able to control our senses and our mind? Looking at these criteria, Jesus qualifies as a *sadhu*, a holy man. Jesus preached a global message, love of God, and also love of brother. This message was beyond any intolerance or selfishness. Jesus was someone who made a tender plea from heart to heart, and that's what makes him such a good Hindu Saint."

I was speechless. I had nothing more to say. This miniature man with an over-sized understanding obviously knew a lot more about Jesus than I did. I didn't need to go to an ashram; I only had to spend a few more hours on the train with this wise man. I was disappointed when he told me he was leaving at the next stop - Bharatpur. "By the way, what is your name, sir, and what do you do?" Perhaps he was a guru. I towered over him when I stood up and nodded, "*Namaste.*" As he gathered his brief-case and newspaper, he looked up at me and proudly announced, "I am Sri Bhatta, and I am a teacher." He nodded, "*Namaste,*" in response, and he was gone in a flash.

Ah yes, I heard that Hindu last names revealed the caste, and most often, the profession of the person. Hindu priests and teachers were exclusively from the Brahman caste – the top of the pyramid and the most privileged. *Brahman* is defined in Hinduism as the concept of the transcendent and immanent, ultimate reality.

It was the Supreme, Cosmic Spirit – thus proving once again that I hit the jackpot in travel companions. Coincidence, chance, or ordained from a higher power? I felt, by far, richer and wiser after my encounter with Sri Bhatta. I also decided to give credit where credit was due.

So, after hearing about Mahatma Gandhi's enlightened opinion, I promoted Jesus to my top prophet and holy man – several notches above the Buddhist's spiritual leader, Siddartha, or the Sikh's Guru Nanar and the Hindu's holy man, Sadhu Adi Shankaracharya.

By now, I felt a great need to balance my chakras. After the traumatic experience of the chaotic New Delhi train station, I felt sluggish, undoubtedly due to blockage of one or more of my energy entry points. However, I knew the danger of opening chakras too fast. I certainly didn't want too much light entering my system too quickly, causing an overload and a possible short circuit.

Yoga would have been the best way to harmonize my chakras, but I opted for my selenite wand due to the lack of space and privacy. Selenite is a form of gypsum that opens the higher chakras of the crown and third eye, plus the powerful Moon Goddess Selene blesses it. It is a memory-strengthening divination stone that guides your path and takes you to your destiny. The selenite crystal's powerful vibration can clear, open, and activate the Crown and higher chakras and is excellent for all spiritual work.

I desperately needed to purify and re-energize my energy centers. While my lips vibrated with forceful *oms*, I took my selenite wand, brushing it through my aura and around my body for a few minutes. The problem with the wand is that if it punctured my aura, holes could allow energy leaks.

A lovely Indian lady, wearing an exquisite emerald green and gold-colored sari, kept glancing over at me from across the aisle. She then got up abruptly and whisked her child up to the first row, where there was a vacant seat. I guess she was preparing to leave at the next scheduled stop. I was very curious because the next stop wasn't for a few hours.

With my chakras balanced, I started to feel hungry and needed fuel immediately. The restaurant car was a few coaches forward, so I reserved my seat with the latest Bollywood magazine and staggered through three jerking cars until I arrived at what looked like a five star Michelin restaurant! Wow!

The sparkling white linen table cloths, napkins, plus fresh flowers decorating the tables, dazzled my senses. The cutlery and long stem glasses were smudge-free; however, there was not a single vacant table. I stood there for a few minutes, wondering if I had to make a reservation when a fair-haired couple asked if I would like to join them. They looked well-traveled and friendly. "Far out, thanks! It's really cool of y'all to invite me to join you." "We so admire your latest hit, `Anticipation.' You are such an epic songwriter, singer, and musician. You have it all." I was tempted to reply, "thanks," and leave it at that. However, I figured the truth would eventually surface.

I introduced myself, "Sorry folks, I'm Marie France from New Orleans, but my friends call me Tyke." They thought I was playing with them. "Come on; we know you're Carly Simon." Well-known musicians were a dime a dozen in India. They all flew in to chill out with their spiritual gurus. "Well, I hate to disappoint y'all, but Carly and I are only look-a-likes. I wish I had her talent." Carly was five foot ten, thin, with long, brown curly hair and a prominent mouth. Her lips were full, and she had a slight overbite. I hoped these disillusioned travelers wouldn't uninvite me.

The guy shook his head, "You are the spittin' image of Carly; we've seen her live many times." He extended his hand, "My name is Damian, and this is my lady, Amber. We're from San Diego but moved to a commune in Oregon before hitting the guru circuit in India." "Groovy, where y'all been hangin' out?" "The past ten months, we've been livin' in Chaurasi Kutia Ashram with Maharishi Mahesh Yogi."

"Cool, if it was good enough for the Beatles, I guess it was the right place to stay cool and get into TM (transcendental meditation). Did you live in the ashram or have your own pad?" "We lived in the ashram, radical digs – full board for 70 rupees ($1) a day." "Out-a-sight!" Amber then commented, "Nifty threads, I just love your Afghan vest and batik scarf."

"Thanks, I found the scarf on Kuta Beach in Bali, only about 25 cents, can you believe?" I played my Bali trump card. Very few hippies had been to Bali yet, and just the mention of that magical isle opened a barrage of questions. "Wow, we've been toying with the idea of making a move from India and heard that Bali was awesome. Can you give us some tips on the best way to get there and where to stay, the hot spots, and the best place to buy Mary Jane (marijuana)?" "Sure, glad to."

5. BURMA-THAILAND-MALAYSIA-SINGAPORE

I advised my newly made diner coach friends to fly into Bangkok. "In case you're heading to Nepal first, fly Royal Nepal Airlines on a Wednesday. There is no connecting flight that day to Bangkok, and the airline will be obliged to put you up for a night in Rangoon. Amazingly enough, Nepal Airlines booked me into the government-owned Strand Hotel. The once-stately landmark is a clone of the famous colonial Raffles Hotel in Singapore but echoes better days." I urged Damian and Amber to go that route. It was worth it. Ne Win, the Prime Minister, was also a military commander and he allowed one-week visas only, and there were military police everywhere. However, I felt safe.

I reflected on my stay there and my vast bedroom with wooden ceiling fans, wooden floors, and dusty furniture. The dining room was the size of a roller skating rink, with at least eighty tables set and only nine people dining. An elderly trio, presumably caught in a time warp, was dressed in well-worn tuxedos from the 40s. They played chamber music as if the Titanic was sinking.

I swooshed across the elegant, empty dance floor, only to be told I had to dress for supper. I asked the waiter to explain how I should dress, and he glared at me and hissed, "With a *dressss*, madam!" I think I flushed and then rushed back to my room to design a dress from my Balinese sarong. I returned to the dining room in a flash, draped with my red batik, off-the-shoulder sarong gown, feeling like a diva without a date. I received an acceptance nod from the waiter, and he ushered me to a table in the back.

Gifted at creating something from nothing, I asked the pianist if he could play Strauss' Blue Danube Waltz. I spotted an elderly gent dining alone and decided to make his day. "Sir, may I have the pleasure of this dance?" I prayed he wasn't paralyzed or had a dislocated hip or worse. He rose to the occasion, clicked his heels, bowed, then lifted my hand elegantly and launched into a waltz that would have inspired Fred Astaire. We whirled and twirled until the very last note, and then he escorted me back to my table. The food was overcooked and bland, English style, so I stuffed myself with bread and retired early.

I informed my train pals, "The main street of Rangoon is lined with crumbling, once magnificent homes since the military take over. After decades of neglect, plus laundry strung haphazardly across the wide columned terraces, I envisioned the final scene in `Gone with the Wind.' Scarlett O'Hara bravely announced, "*Tomorrow is another day,*" which made sense and became my motto. I had just enough time to visit a Buddhist Pagoda and the ornate Rangoon City Hall before my time was up, and I jogged back to the airport bus. Yes, be sure and visit at least one pagoda and City Hall. Just ignore the military police in the streets with their mean-looking weapons!"

* * *

Damian asked me, "What's about Bangkok? Is it groovy?" I admitted, "Not my scene, but if you like massages, noise and pollution, go for it. I think two or three days max. Once you've seen the Grand Palace (official digs of the Kings of Siam), the Wat Pho Buddist Temple (home of the humongous gold-leafed reclining Buddha), and the floating market, you can head south to Malaysia. Nevertheless, I must admit that the food is a dream and a semi-chic hotel with air conditioning is only $5."

I couldn't help but remember the impact of being surrounded by droves of monks and monk-ettes wandering around Bangkok. Their colorful presence and disciplined devotion fascinated me. The spice-colored robes they wore were blends of delicious shades of curry, cumin, paprika, turmeric, and blazing saffron orange. I sought out a monk shop and bought a curry-colored sash to give my travel outfits some pizzazz. Female monks are obliged to shave their heads and eyebrows like the monks, thus counting me out.

* * *

I recommended that my travel companions head south to Malaysia overland. "The cheapest and best transport I found was a funky, shared taxi, with the possibility to stop en route to Singapore." My driver was cross-eyed and smoked something toxic, but I had the window wide open and a scarf over my nose. I swapped tips and snacks with other travelers, and we all agreed to swing over to the island of Penang, the `Pearl of the Orient.' Then it was just a twenty-minute ferry across the strait to the sparkling island.

I explained, "The peaceful collision of cultures and religions creates a unique, utopian atmosphere in Penang. There is a good mix of Buddhists, Muslims, Christians, Hindus, Taoists, and other Chinese religions. The overload of temples, mosques, and churches decorating the landscape gives a multi-faceted tribute to the one and only God." Damian nodded in agreement, "Ditto, that's our philosophy; all roads evidently lead to one God."

"Ah yes, the Botanical Gardens are a tropical groove, but watch out for the feral monkeys that can be vicious. Don't forget to wash your lips, so they don't smell traces of aromas from your previous meals. The vipers at Snake Park are charming but remember to leave time for the soft, sandy beaches and a dip in the Indian Ocean," I added.

"I don't recommend my hotel, *The Pearl*, which it clearly is not. My room consisted of only a single lumpy bed, a hand basin that leaked, and no phone, so I stopped at reception the night before my departure to ask for a wake-up call at 7 am. That way, I would have time to arrive at a pre-paid, round-trip ferry in plenty of time. I woke up with the morning light flooding my room and looked at my watch. What a bummer! It was 7:40 am, and my ferry was leaving in twenty minutes. I jumped into my clothes, grabbed my sack, and went flip-flopping towards the ferry." Amber smiled, "I would have done likewise."

"The owner abandoned his post and galloped behind me, yelling, `bad hippie, you did not give me my ringgits' (Malaysian currency). He shouted other stuff in his native tongue that I didn't understand, fortunately. Without turning my head, I screamed, `You didn't wake me up'! I skidded up to the dock and jumped onto the moving boat, panting and shocked that I made it aboard."

I admitted, "Once settled on the ferry, I reflected on the Keystone Cops chase. I feel remorseful that I didn't pay the man, but I didn't have time, or I'd have missed my ferry. I wonder if my misdemeanor will affect my karma?" Damian chuckled and comforted me, "No way, the owner had better worry about his karma."

* * *

"The shared, unmarked taxi was there on time, but with a different mix of passengers waiting to board. I grabbed the passenger seat since I was the longest and fastest and looked forward to the four-hour ride to Kuala Lumpur." I briefed Damian and Amber, "You'll only need a day or two in the capital, and my `must-see' suggestion is the Batu Cave Temple. The Hindu Shrines and statues in the cave draw pilgrims from across Asia and date back to the Neolithic times."

Urging them not to miss the shrine, I explained, "It's dramatically positioned in a steep limestone cliff, almost three-hundred steps straight up. The climb is sweaty but meaningful. There's a humongous gold statue of the Tamil war god, Murugan, glaring at you as you enter the cave. Trance festivals are held there each December."

I'd also recommended, "Take in the original Chinese Quarter on Petaling St. You'll freak out with all the cool shops and fab eats. Check out the Islamic Arts Museum and the oldest Cantonese Temple in the city, Guan Di Temple, and then you can head south. Hotels there are cheap and clean."

* * *

"Singapore is only four and a half hours from Kuala Lumpur. Whoa, when you head towards the center of the city, with all the skyscrapers, you'll have the feeling you're in Zurich. No litter on the sidewalks or streets, buildings are outrageously clean, and all the Singaporeans looked like they just stepped out of Vogue magazine." I was impressed by how precision chic and petite they were, with slim figures that screeched 'designer.' It was a déjà vu of arriving in Paris. I warned Damian and Amber, "I read that you can be arrested for chewing gum on the street and shot for spitting it out."

I advised my friends not to smoke any joints, clean out their stash before arriving there, and fly south quickly. I also suggested that they disguise themselves as nerds. "The airport control men are square and not into guys with long hair and sandals. So, you'd better clean up your act before the flight. The alternative is to travel through Sumatra overland." I explained to Damian and Amber that I was too itchy to get to my long-awaited destination and destiny, so I flew.

6. BALI

Then I revealed, "I made it through customs with my hair pulled back in a low braid and a clean pair of jeans with a normal white blouse." I remember how uncomfortable I was. I felt like such a gawky minority among all those neat, chic, look-a-like Asians. I had only known of one Chinese family that lived in the French Quarter in New Orleans. They had a family laundry business across from my mom's art gallery, and their children were working the cash register by the time they could reach the counter. They always nodded, wore laughing smiles, and bought everything by cash, including the three-floor building that housed their laundry. Rumor had it they laundered more than clothes. Who cares? They were industrious.

Politely, I asked Damian and Amber, "Do you have time to hear about my adventures in Bali, or do you prefer I just jot down the pertinent details?" I could see they were "hooked," and I was a raconteur by nature. "No, we `wanna' hear more," replied Amber, "We know our own stories by heart, and we're a bit bored. That's why we asked you to join us. We thought you looked like you could entertain us."

"Okay, guys, here's the full-blown story. After making it through customs, I worked my way down the narrow aisle of Garuda Airlines, looking for a free seat. Voilà, row twelve, my lucky number. I discovered that the neat young Singaporean girl, seated at the window, spoke better English than I did. During the three hour flight to Bali's capital, Na Lin and I discovered that we were born, not only in the same year but on the same exact date! Besides that, we both had dogs of the same breed with the same name, and we both majored in Fine Arts."

Starting to freak out, I had wondered if the plane was flying through the twilight zone. "I was curious if my seatmate was telling the truth. She was. She showed me her passport, and it was Na Lin who started talking about her Dachshund named Penny. We decided we were obviously twins in a previous life and just left it at that." "Yeah," Amber nodded in agreement, "I have a spiritual twin from a previous life also, I can relate."

I described Na Lin to them as being petite, with jet black hair to her shoulders and long bangs. She has a perfect, miniature figure and is always well dressed. I explained that since she had a month's vacation from her high-powered job at a lawyer's office in downtown Singapore and I had no schedule, we decided to look for a small bungalow to rent on Kuta Beach. Her Australian surfer friends, who ride the big waves in Bali every year, bragged about the ultra-cheap bungalows on that deserted beach. Damian was intrigued. "Sounds like the perfect plan for us!"

"The plane touches down in the small southern capital of Denpasar. Bali is deemed the most spectacular of the seventeen thousand Indonesian islands." I became lost in my thoughts, remembering how Na Lin and I split a taxi for the short ride southwest to Kuta Beach. I could hardly take it in. I had REALLY made it to my destination! I had arrived at BALI, known as the Land of Gods. This had been my dream for the past six months, as I worked my way across Europe and down from Thailand. I pinched myself until I yelped. Then I started to sing, *"Bali Ha'i,"* from South Pacific, and it helped me decompress until I began to laugh so hard, tears flowed.

I guess it all began in Ibiza when I asked `Beautiful Barry' if he knew of an unparalleled paradise that I might visit in my quest to explore the world. Without hesitation, he shot back, Bali. I asked him what it was like, but he didn't know anyone who had been there yet. However, he heard from a friend of a friend that it was the `coolest' place ever. I trusted Barry's opinion.

Damian and Amber pleaded, "Then what?" "Ah yes, Na Lin instructed the driver to drop us off at Janeek's Restaurant. The owner of the informal café greeted us with a wide grin that flaunted her large, snowy-white teeth and made us feel genuinely welcome. Janeek's specialty was pancakes and magic mushroom omelet; however, her spicy Nasi Goreng carried the fame of being the best on the island. After our gourmet meal at that homely, little, hand-made restaurant, she asked us if we were looking for a place to stay."

Janeek's entrepreneurial skills excelled, and I was pleased that Na Lin did the negotiating for our beach house. She glanced over to me to check if 85,000 rupiahs ($6) was okay. I thought, hmmm, six dollars a day is a bit pricey. My newly acquired soul-mate winked and said that $6 was for the entire month of September. Janeek asked her young dishwasher to escort us to the house.

I explained to my train pals that our bungalow was quite impressive and seemed thoroughly organic. The walls were brick and stone with thatch roofing, and the bed frames and kitchen/dining table were teak wood. It was simple and clean with three spacious bedrooms and even had an indoor bathroom! Eureka, we hit gold! However, Na Lin noticed there was a small hitch – no running water or electricity.

The boy said that he was included in the price. He would draw four buckets of water each evening and carry them to the kitchen, and then he'd light the five oil lamps. I thought, come on, is this for real, $6 a month, including a servant boy? We looked at each other in disbelief and then sealed the deal with a hug. We paid the money upfront, as Janeek explained she had been cheated quite often by ghetto hippies.

Damian and Amber were taking it all in. As I spoke, I jotted the key info down for them, along with detailed directions. They admitted they were ready for a carefree sabbatical from the disciplined ashram life and communal living. They couldn't wait to meet Janeek and request the same cottage we had and try her magic mushroom omelet.

I informed them, "There's not a single hotel on the entire Kuta Beach, and very few surfers remain after the holidays." Then I rambled on about how the Aussies had returned home for school or work until their next mid-term break or Christmas. After all, Bali is the backyard playground for the Australians. European tourism hadn't taken off yet, and only some retired Dutch, leftover from the colonial days, could be spotted in the local shops and cafes in the nearby village of Seminyak. Indonesia gained its independence from the Dutch in 1949, a mere twenty-two years ago, but you can see the locals gradually shaking off those shackles and beginning to shine.

Remembering how Na Lin and I were on the beach within minutes, I was ecstatic to catch up with my daily yoga Sun Salutations and breathing exercises. Ahhh, I sighed, "Does life get any better than this?" Actually, it did. A sun-baked local came strolling by with fresh, green coconuts and a machete. Upon demand, he whacked off the tops and handed us a straw to extract the refreshing coconut water. The immature white meat was still soft and tasted like almonds.

Ah, I recall how I dozed off for a brief nap, only to be awakened by a barefoot lady promoting head massages and lice removal. For pennies, I indulged in both. She was disappointed not to find any lice in my thick, wavy, waist-long hair, and I promised her I'd try to do better next time. We remained on the beach until the explosive burst of color accompanied the sun's last gasp before slipping into the Indian Ocean. A few *oms*, then home. Damian and Amber looked dreamy-eyed, and their mouths remained ajar.

I proudly reported to them that our bungalow had its very own temple with five shrines. That seemed to be the norm in Bali. Ganesha, the elephant god, is the supreme deity in the Balinese Hinduism tradition, and easy to spot the benign elephant head on top of a chubby, boyish body. He protects houses and decorates Bali's temples from north to south. All local homes had fresh flowers sacrificed to temple gods and a never-ending supply of incense that permeated the thick, humid air, to such an extent that I hoped it would suffocate the mosquitoes instead of me.

Bali is the only Hindu-majority province in Indonesia, strictly adhering to Agama Hindu Dharma, a unique blend of Hinduism with a pinch of Buddhism. The Balinese beliefs were intertwined into the fabric of their lives. Secularism didn't exist. Their ancient dance, dynamic and intensely expressive, was part of their religious ritual, as was the Monkey Chant dance. These rituals were accompanied by bronze and bamboo xylophones, gongs, chimes, cymbals, bells, drums and bamboo rattles.

I confessed to my train buddies, "Unless you are drugged, stoned, or high on magic mushrooms, the frenzied tempo of that combination will make your eyes pop out." The performances we attended were strictly religious, and we were the only foreigners in attendance, invited by Janeek. I pretended to go with the flow and gave rave reviews. However, I honestly felt it was driving me to the edge of no return, and I avoided further performances.

The good thing with Na Lin, we did our own thing and often went our separate ways in discovering the island at our own pace. When we were together, we didn't need to speak much since we were on the same wavelength.

Also, our completely different physiques enabled us to avoid competition. We were in two different leagues. It was impossible to compete in attracting the same guys. Either they were into tall, hippie-looking string beans, or they were drawn to petite, classical Asians. Nevertheless, between us, we had something for everyone and made a great odd-couple.

There was only one four-star luxury hotel on the island with air conditioning, electricity, running water, and even a swimming pool. You might wonder why a hotel needed a pool unless you tried to swim off the southwest coast of Bali during the wrong moon phase. I foolishly took a plunge during the new moon gravitation pull. It seems there are `swell rolls' at that time of the moon calendar, and rip currents are triggered. "Hey guys, do you want to hear about my swimming escapade?" "Yes, yes, everything is so amazing, bring it on."

I explained to them that I was a good swimmer, but I was not into extreme sports, so I was obliged to call on my collection of deities, trying to form a mental mantra. I wasn't prepared to exit planet earth yet; I still had too much to do. When I finally surfaced through the pounding swell, I thought I was caught in seaweed. I desperately needed air within seconds, and there was a thick carpet between my face and life-saving oxygen. It was my crowning glory, my pounds of wavy hair, that betrayed me.

I floundered in shallow water, like a beached mermaid, trying to catch my breath. Meanwhile, a handful of happy tourists gazed on without concern.

My hair remained in a braid for future swims, and I avoided new moon and full moon dips. Janeek laughed and said, "Oh, you must always ask a local fisherman before you go swimming off Kuta or Canggu beaches."

Only twenty minutes southwest by auto-rickshaw and we were at the luxury hotel, walking through the volcanic sand of Senur Beach. It was not as awesome as Kuta, but a change. "Do we need to see Senur Beach?" asked Damian. "No, it's nothing exceptional. The sea and sand are better at Kuta, only if you want to try the hotel's buffet or need a dip in their chlorinated pool. One dip and you won't need a bath for at least a week."

Na Lin and I were amazed to find Little Italy at the lunch buffet in the hotel. At least twenty Italians were there making a film with Celeste as the stunning lead. She had the box office hit, "Fiji," and was now in demand. With a few cat-calls and whistles, the crew coaxed us to join them. Just some innocent fun - the Italians were so exaggerated and over-the-top, we couldn't resist joining them. "Hey, do you two wanna hear about the Italians and the places we visited?" "Of course, don't skip anything!"

I filled them in with all the details, explaining that Alessandro, the head cameraman, had swept Na Lin off her feet. I became good friends with Celeste and the producer, Flavio Ravioli, a real hunk, but real gay. The leading male, Lorenzo, was stuck on himself, and I certainly didn't want him to come unglued. Every other day or so, we joined the crew, cast, and producer to discovered a new part of the island. They filmed scenes in all the best spots.

The first stop was Ubud, the cultural headquarters and the heart of the island. Alessandro (nicknamed Sandro) picked us up in his courtesy car at 6 am, since cameras rolled an hour later. The village of Ubud is eighteen miles north of Kuta, in the uplands of Bali, known as the center for traditional crafts and dance. However, it was much more than that. It was an eruption of creativity. It wasn't as if some of the villagers were born with an artistic flair; it was matter-of-fact that everyone could paint, carve, sculpt, and dance.

Even the smallest kids sported a carving knife or a paintbrush. Tiny girls practiced religious dances with precision, often in full regalia and eye make-up. Not even Walt Disney could have imagined such a 'land, 'or it would have been the largest attraction in his Orange County, Disneyland. He could have even included a volcanic lava ride.

I couldn't help but reflect on the classes offered for the Legong Dance. As long as it wasn't the Monkey Chant Dance, I thought I'd give it a go. There were two advanced dancers, one Mexican, and the other French. I'd have to put up with the wretched, rapid, bonging noise of someone hammering on a xylophone.

After seeing the dance several times, I knew the basic movements. It consisted of the art of keeping your neck rigid while jerking your head to the left and right and darting your eyes right to left. Then you had to sway your arms, hands, and fingers gracefully while sticking out your buttocks and lifting your feet (one at a time). The trick is, keeping your feet flat, turning your toes outwards, and heels downwards. It was like juggling five hot potatoes at the same time.

Anyway, the worst thing that could happen was I'd look like a klutzy tourist. I was wearing a sarong with a wide belt and a tight sleeveless t-shirt, so that worked. I followed the leader and did surprisingly well, except I had an eye ache and was drenched from the relentless heat.

It was a relief to go for a scenic ride to get out of the heat and forget the brain-rattling bongs. A lush rain forest surrounds Ubud. The terraced rice paddies, speckled with Hindu temples and shrines, decorated the landscape, sucking the breath right out of my lungs. Nearby was the "Elephant Cave" with carved Goa Gajah and Gunung Kawi, with its rock-cut shrines.

Also, Mount Agung, an active volcano, was only eighteen miles from Ubud. It's the highest point on the island and dominates the surrounding area, influencing climate, especially rainfall patterns. While I was there, it drizzled, and then the sun came bursting through the clouds, painting a vivid rainbow across the heavens.

Working up a good vibrato always gives me the same internal therapeutic massage that my mantras do. There is something about vocal vibration that recalibrates my spirit and soul without bruising my aura. The film crew was loyal and always applauded after one of my outbursts.

"Yeah, we studied vocal yoga and synthesizing techniques at the ashram," Amber chirped with a smile. "It always harmonizes my chakras."

"I decided to offer my services to the Italian crew," I boasted. "I proposed giving them free yoga classes since they had been so generous and kind to us, toting us around to all their 'shoots.' I offered two, two-hour sessions twice a week, and they took the bait. I scheduled the classes before lunch, at their hotel beach, so it would seem natural to stay on for lunch. Yep, it worked like a charm." "Clever lady," approved Amber.

"Starting with some basic positions, I knew full well that my yoga experience might not have been vast. However, their experience was zero. My French bikinis were a hit, and I used to tie myself in knots to wake them up before we started. I had the edge and taught with confidence."

I confessed, "The results were often hilarious! I practiced self-control, and if I started to laugh, I transformed it into a vibrating chant. I adored giving yoga classes, and my students were no worse off for it. I told them to practice their Sun Salutations each morning upon rising and not to forget their breathing exercises, preferably on the beach. Inhaling the fresh ocean air 2-3-4 and exhaling all negativity 2-3-4 - repeat, repeat, repeat, and repeat."

Then I explained how glad we were when the film shoots moved south to Bukit Peninsula, only twelve miles south of Kuta Beach. One of the major temples founded in the 11th century became the haunting backdrop to the film's dramatic ending. Na Lin had quite a few `extra' roles, as she easily passed for an Indonesian. I only had a few, as there was not a great demand for hippies in the film. I described how I got to stagger around the beach, looking drugged and then fall into the ocean and drown. I did it with a dramatic flair.

Meanwhile, we coaxed the crew to dine at Janeek's place, at least three or four evenings a week. Kuta started to rock. Italians are addicted to their pasta, but we encouraged them to try Janeek's nasi goreng and even magic mushroom omelets. By then, my recipe for "banana split" had worked its way up to the top as the dessert in demand. The Italians loved the restaurant, meanwhile boosting Janeek's earnings tenfold. They were extravagantly generous and outrageously boisterous, but we all had a blast, and Janeek gained fame and fortune.

Our month was coming to an end, and the crew insisted on throwing us a farewell party. Little did they know I become unpredictable with half a glass of wine. I grabbed a pepper mill like a mic, leaped onto the nearest table, and launched into the only Italian song I knew, Dean Martin's "That's Amore." I sang about the moon hitting their eye, like a giant Pizza Pie and everyone joined in. Wine flowed, and dancing broke out - the Italians know how to party!

Admittedly, my Italian was very basic, but I could communicate with flamboyant body language. Ciao, like *namasta*, serves for hello, as well as good-bye. *Ciao bella* and *ciao bello* are more intimate greetings & salutations. *Belissima* (beautiful f), *belissimo* (beautiful m), *cosi cosi* (like this), *mangiare* (to eat), *dormire* (to sleep), *per favore* (please), *grazie* (thank you). It was amazing that with such a limited vocabulary, we were able to communicate perfectly well. After eating and drinking ourselves into oblivion, we hugged and kissed cheek to cheek, then exchanged addresses - vowing to reconnect in Rome. Flavio Ravioli, the merry and gay producer, insisted that I come to stay with him in Rome. I agreed.

Damian and Amber were sold on Bali, but Amber asked, "Are there any dangerous animals or things we should beware of?" "Dangerous, hmmm, I'd say the most dangerous thing is tap water. Avoid it like the plague. Dangerous animals? I guess the mosquito, then the stray dogs (if they get into a pack), Bali jellyfish, water snakes, and of course, the Temple monkeys," I admitted.

"I didn't have any negative encounters because I wore lemon eucalyptus essential oil against mosquitoes, lavender paired with cedarwood, and a dab of lemon to calm wild dogs. It also works on calming jellyfish and snakes. The best against Temple monkeys is a slap on their paws when no one is looking. Just don't go in December or January, 'cause that's the rainy season."

Meanwhile, Na Lin and I had become best friends and real soulmates during that intense month of sea, sand, culture, beauty, fun, adventure, and mutual self-awareness revelations. Before leaving our bungalow, we placed some flowers onto our house shrines, not wanting to offend the ancestral gods.

After embracing Janeek with accolades of appreciation and telling our pals, the beach freaks, good-bye, we hopped into a taxi to the airport. Na Lin was light-hearted and in love, and I was digesting the month's events as we boarded Ganesha Airways for Singapore. I stayed with Na Lin in Singapore for a week before flying to Kathmandu via Bangkok and Rangoon. We know, without a doubt, that our paths will cross again. It is our destiny.

I told Damian and Amber that I had a ton of Balinese stories but would wrap it up due to our impending arrival at their destination, Shamgarh. I was glad I scooped up a handful of mom's art gallery cards so that I could distribute them to all my friends of the cosmos. A bit more class than a scrap of paper, and I knew my mother would eventually forward any letters or news that made it to her. Damian and Amber thanked me profusely for the tips and tales and then nodded with *Namaste*. I followed suit, then split.

With another eight hours to the Bombay Central Station, I decided to find a spot to snooze. Presto, I found two empty seats together, so I curled up in a fetal position and practiced Pranayama, yoga breathing exercises until I drifted off into a blissful sleep. Six hours later, I awoke with the excitement of discovering the infamous mega-metropolis of Bombay, home of the film industry, the Elephant caves, opium dens, and the gateway to India. I wouldn't stay more than two days since I wanted to take the coastal ferry down to Goa, arriving just in time for Christmas.

7. BOMBAY

As I stepped down onto the platform, I realized that the chaotic New Delhi train station was only a stepping stone in preparation for what I was to experience. The population of Bombay in 1971 was a mere 6,500,000, perhaps double the size of New Delhi. I longed to have Arjun holding my hand, leading me out of this inferno. I called on my higher power, my assigned angels, and whoever else was listening. Bombay was called the City of Dreams, but so far, it was a nightmare. At least twenty ragged kids swamped me screaming *baksheesh, baksheesh* (gift, gift). If I started handing out rupees, I would only draw another twenty or more begging kids.

Feeling led by an omnipresent power, I chose the tallest boy, who was jumping up and down like a human pogo stick, trying to get my attention. I boldly announced as I grasped his arm, "This is my boy. You will have to find another tourist." It worked, my boy started screaming to the other children to back off, and they scattered. They immediately pounced on the next tourist. Mafia tactics, you paid off one kid to protect you from the rest. The protection money was well worth it and affordable.

These kids grew up on the streets and were from the massive slum district but drifted to the city's profitable areas during the day. It was heart-breaking, but you needed a system to survive. I said "hotel" and did a pantomime of "sleep," and my boy led me to an auto-rickshaw and directed the driver to the Taj Mahal Palace Hotel near India's Gateway. He introduced himself as Harsh, Hindu for "joy" or "happiness," which seemed hardly applicable, but he was grinning ear to ear.

India's caste system was so ingrained into the land's culture that even the untouchables accepted their lot in life. It seemed that whatever caste you were born into, you remained there, and only certain types of work were allotted to each stratum. The opulent Taj Palace Hotel stood out like a pompous, sore thumb, boasting the glory of the British Raj coloni-al-era; everything Gandhi peacefully fought against as he led the suppressed nation to their independence in 1947. However, the high caste Hindus seemed just as oppressive, if not worse than arrogant Brit-ish colonialists.

I told Harsh, "Not enough money for Taj Hotel, cheap hotel." He understood and led me to a nearby dilapidated hostel. There were a few backpackers at the reception, so I thought it must be okay. I paid Harsh double for his trouble and was grateful for his help. I asked the guys if they could recommend a decent place to eat, and they invited me to join them. "Thanks, guys, I'll just get rid of my stuff."

After checking in, I left my travel bag in the barren room and grabbed my saffron, good luck Buddhist sash, and slipped the strap of my fringed leather bag over my head and across my heart. Shedding my cut-offs, I donned my ankle-length bell-bottoms and was back down in the lobby before you could say "Jack Robinson." That was the plus of traveling alone; you connected when you were in the mood or went your own way.

"Hi, I'm Steve, and this is my friend Dan, we're from Vancouver. We took a leave of absence for six months from our UBC studies to home in on South Asia. I'm doing my thesis on the Indian Subcontinent, and Dan is collecting info for his masters in geology."

"Sounds intriguing, I'm Marie France from New Orleans, but my friends call me Tyke. I'm here on a spiritual journey." "Cool, how long are you staying in Bombay?" "Only two days, since I'm heading to Goa for Christmas. I have lots of friends from Ibiza who are meeting up there."

"Cool, how about some *vada pav, panipuri,* or *dahl puri?*" "Out-a-sight!" I liked Indian food, and whatever they said, I was up for it. "There's a restaurant just a few blocks away that's clean and cheap."

"Awesome!" I felt like I was with two Boy Scout leaders, and we were on our way to roast hot dogs over an open fire. They say you can't tell a book by its cover, but I felt I was with the "Hardy Boys."

We were the only foreigners in the restaurant, so that was a good sign. Eat where the locals eat. The food was mouth-watering and delivered a good spicy kick. We doused everything with Tabasco sauce in New Orleans, so I was used to crying into my food. I was fool-heartedly polite in asking Steve about his thesis.

"Oh, glad you asked. It is on a radically interesting topic. Did you know that India was still a part of the supercontinent called Gondwana some one hundred and forty million years ago?" I shook my head, "No," and regretted asking. "Gondwana was composed of South America, Africa, Antarctica, and Australia. When this supercontinent split up, a tectonic plate comprising India and modern Madagascar started to drift away. India split from Madagascar and drifted north-east colliding with Asia fifty million years ago.

"India is still moving at about eighteen inches a year, with resistance from Eurasia's plate." "Wow," I feigned interest, "I guess that's how the Himalayan range was formed - from the impact." Steve's eyes lit up, and he said I took the words right out of his mouth.

I thought I would inject some fun into their humdrum existence, "Hey, why don't we catch a film? The Indian extravaganzas are so amazingly kitsch." Steve and Dan shrugged and said they preferred to check out an opium den if I'd like to come along. I couldn't believe my ears, these two boy scouts in an opium den?

"Ah, okay, but I don't do drugs. Of course, it's part of the Bombay color, so yeah, I'm in." As we strolled to the nearby "den district," Dan told me they wanted to visit all of South Asia, so they still had five countries to explore. They had already covered Ceylon and said it was a groove.

Steve confessed, "I've been looking forward to experiencing an opium den since I read a fascinating book about the Opium Wars that raged from 1839 until 1860. The British East India Company was the leading supplier of opium to China. They cleverly preferred using opium grown on India's conquered lands to sell to China since they made a killing on the tax revenue.

"Finally, China got fed up, so they legalized opium and started to grow their own poppies and outstripped the Indian-grown supplies." Dan asked me, "Haven't you read *The Picture of Dorian Gray*, by Oscar Wilde? The quays of East End London were rife with low-end dens. It seems it was the fashion among authors and poets of the day. A few puffs won't hurt anything." The street was chock full of dens. "Eenie, meenie, miney, mo, let's go for number five."

Like walking into a derelict arena of sleaze, there was a shabby glamour about the whole set-up. It was a dark blend of exotic pipes, and people strewn around the floor on slightly raised platforms enveloped in an opiate fog. A bearded Chinese in traditional dress was preparing the paraphernalia, and his wife, I presume, collected the fee.

It was evident that people had to recline. It was the only position they could hold the long opium pipes over the oil lamps that would heat the drug until it vaporized, allowing the smoker to inhale the vapors. I could feel my chakras blocking and the negative vibrations encroaching already.

I told Steve and Dan I would wait for them outside. I repeatedly breathed in deeply and then exhaled the negativity. I followed up with my favorite mantra and the Lord's Prayer while clinging to my Mary medal. I felt peace from above melt and dissolve any gloom, clarifying all darkness and restoring my composure. I would give my aura a thorough cleansing when I got back to the hotel. I could identify that lost people were trying to fill a God-shaped hole in their weary souls.

Twenty minutes later, Steve and Dan exited from the den muttering, "Over-rated rip-off. I think we got tourist prices. Well, we can scratch that off our list." Actually, I was glad that I went in to check it out, so I could brag about being in an opium den - of course, I wasn't quite sure who I would impress.

As we strolled back to the hostel, Dan philosophically explicated, "Bombay equals tolerance and open-mindedness. If you have talent, ambition, money, or beauty, you can make it in Bombay." I could relate; it looked like multitudes of rural, young hopefuls flocked to Dream City as if a magnet of hope pulled them.

With only one full day left to discover Bombay's sights, I preferred to go alone. I carefully chose the Elephant Caves as a priority before heading south. They were a collection of cave temples predominantly dedicated to the Hindu god Shiva. They were located on Elephanta Island, in Bombay Harbor, just seven miles east of the city. I figured it was worth the trip, so I splurged on an auto-rickshaw and didn't regret my decision.

After lunch, I found refuge in the Mahatma Gandhi Museum. After all, he was the people's people. Gandhi was the counter-culture activist who dressed bohemian simple, defying his status as an intellect, lawyer, politician, freedom fighter, and architect of a form of non-violent civil disobedience that would influence the world. The tiny man grew into a giant force for civil rights, and he courageously fought against discrimination.

In 1915, Gandhi founded an ashram open to all castes. Having embraced Jainism since childhood, he believed in non-violence, fasting, meditation, and vegetarianism. He adopted a life of simplicity, austerity, fasting, and celibacy – free of material possessions. Mahatma means "great soul," and he had one of the greatest.

I realized that even though most of Bombay was Hindu, there were Muslims, Christians, Sikhs, Buddhists, Jews, Jains, and tribal religions, giving the city a kaleidoscopic community atmosphere. I read that Hindus believed that "all religions are good." They shared values common to all faiths; piety, love of God, respect for tradition, and stress on duty and responsibility. They adhered to the essential human virtues; non-violence, truthfulness, compassion, and charity.

Hinduism is considered the most tolerant religion – a monastic and open-minded religion that even considers Christians as Brahmans. Of course, there are always a few rotten eggs in the bunch. You'll find extremists and fanatics that stray from their original teachings within all religions and allow septic zeal to seep into their original enlightenment. Yes, there is a spiritual battle of good versus evil going on - light versus darkness. But I believe, when you let the light in, it *will* swallow all darkness.

At first, I was disappointed to have only two days in Bombay; however, I figured the only way to remain in Bombay was to have a strategy to deal with the heartbreak you witnessed daily. I didn't have it. I was glad to be leaving the next morning. The multitude of poverty-stricken beggars, who ventured from their slum dwellings each morning, swamping the city center in search of food or rupees, was more than I could bear. Something was terribly wrong with the caste system and the plight of those "untouchables" who numbly reached out into a void. I vowed to myself that I would not forget them when I grew up and had the means to make a difference.

* * *

I was advised to buy a ticket at the pier on Dockyard Road, where the morning ferry was leaving for Goa at 10 am. I arrived early in eager anticipation. After purchasing my upper-deck ticket, I stood at the front of a long line until the gates opened onto the gangplanks. Then, as they flung open the gates, I dashed for a life raft to claim it with my shawl. "Hash-Hank" had given me that helpful tip back on Freak Street. The passengers collectively created a multi-hued representation of happiness. The vibrant colors of the local ladies saris ricocheted off the boat's newly varnished wood into a prismatic hallelujah.

Our boat, the Klonkan Shakti, was a microscopic world of its own, a true melting pot of cultures and faces. About a fifth of the passengers were hippies, toting guitars and picnic baskets. I didn't recognize anyone from Ibiza, but I imagined they were already scattered on Goa's beaches. I wore my hand-embroidered cut-off jeans and a smocked top that I could pull down off my shoulders, plus a colorful shawl to wrap up in for the night or attach at my waist like a skirt. It made a versatile travel outfit.

I took a deeper than deep breath, breathing in the surrounding harmony, and exhaled the noise, pollution and chaos of Bombay, followed by a prayer of thanksgiving. The canvas roof, supported by bamboo poles, partially shaded the upper deck from the sun's intense rays, enabling me to secure a shady spot, so I sat there in a lotus position, protecting my space.

A frizzy-haired guy, draped with a guitar, carried a harmonica, and I was sure of what the Bob Dylan look-a-like would probably sing. Two other guys wore guitars, and an Indian was lugging a sitar that was more or less his size. I envisioned a floating Woodstock aboard our Klonkan vessel. The 'bucket man' came around with a bucket piled high with Limcas and Thumbs Up – India's answer to Seven-up and Coca Cola. The bell sounded for lunch, so those of us without a picnic hamper bought lunch coupons. We were served an out-of-this-world fish curry with fish that tasted so fresh they probably hopped directly out of the Arabian Sea and into the Chief's pot.

After lunch, some life rafts were turned upside down to be used as card tables or diaper change stations. Music was brewing at the other end of the deck, and I was drawn by a pied piper playing a Jethro Tull tune. I decided to check it out and went to see if I could jam with the musicians or perhaps vocalize.

I had a Martin acoustic guitar that I strummed my way through high school and college while miming Joan Baez's super vibrato. I also did some fancy tambourine shaking while imitating James Brown's groovy zigzag slide. I would see if opportunity knocked. Yep, the Dylan guy adjusted the harmonica brace around his neck and started with the song about the Tambourine Man, followed by other Dylan hits. By now, they passed around Feni (liquor made in Goa from cashew), and people were loosening up.

A redheaded hippie mom started to strum and sing, "Hey, let the sunshine. . . " and I chimed along in harmony. Someone pushed me forward, and we had a duet going, then everyone joined in. The group shouted, "More songs from `Hair,'" so we dove in!

A group of devout Catholic locals headed home to Goa were reciting the rosary and praying (probably for us). I asked my singing partner if she knew Joan Baez's version of "Amazing Grace," and she did.

As Maya strummed, I belted out that grace-saturated song that moved strong men to tears. Some of the Indian Christians on board knew all the words and joined in. I was able to imitate Joan Baez's vibrato - it made me feel like I was flying. Singing stimulates the production of feel-good endorphins, and the vibration produced as we sang released an "*om* mantra" sense of peace. The upper deck might have been a bit more expensive; however, what I experienced was priceless.

We positioned ourselves facing west to take in the sunset while this little world unto itself plugged on to Goa. The refreshment man had run out of Limca, so now we were drinking Feni with fresh lime water, and after the fourth round of Feni, the talk turned to God and love and who made the best cashew liquor in Goa. Goan spirit at its best!

Along the Konkan coast, when it was getting dark, the ship pulled in nearer to shore. Large hand-rowed canoes would leave the harbors of the coastal villages to transport passengers to our boat. I was amazed how well even the older passengers navigated the rope ladder precariously dangling off the side of the boat. The same experienced boatmen would then take the disembarking passengers to the shore in like-wise fashion.

The rafts that had doubled as game tables, bar counters, and diaper changing stations were converted into beds. Somewhere in the night, we'd pass the sister ship, and a horn blast from one Captain to the other would give the signal that all was well. This was true community; I could have remained on that `love boat' forever.

We awoke with the rising sun's soft rays, and I spotted a small group who had already started their Sun Salutations. I joined in smooth unison, and we felt unified by our mutual beliefs and joint flexibility. I could see the palm-lined Goan coastline's silhouette and felt like I was finally arriving home to be reunited with my "Ibizan family."

At about 9:00 am, we sailed past Chapora Fort, then Anjuna Beach, followed by the picturesque Jesuit retreat at its peak. Onwards we chugged to Calangute and finally, the grand entry up the Mandove River.

8. GOA

Goa had been a Portuguese colony for nearly four hundred and fifty years. Hence the inhabitants of the region had absorbed the culture and submitted to the conversion to Catholicism. Their descendants are normally referred to as Goan Catholics, and an overwhelming majority are of Konkani ethnicity. Goa semi-merged into India in 1961, only a decade before I arrived. Twenty-eight Catholic churches remained. I wondered why the locals were so tolerant in accepting an avalanche of scruffy hippies, zonked out on drugs, to overrun their golden beaches.

When the ferry docked, I was reluctant to disembark. If the past twenty-four hours was not Nirvana, it was the closest I had come, or perhaps the trip was a mirage created by the ecstasy of escaping Bombay. There was a bus waiting, and most of us hippies jumped on and got off at Calangute Beach, and the rest went on to Anjuna Beach.

Most of us free-spirited travelers in Goa were westerners looking for freedom from our frenetic pace. We were fed-up with competing in the rat race and preferred to indulge in a lifestyle that allowed peace and reflection—what better place than the beaches of Goa. Besides, you could buy hash and marijuana for a song. Pay zero for heating, and cheap beach house rentals were a dime a dozen.

I wore my three-foot-long mass of hair free and frizzy, adorned with a headband I had woven together with suede strips, stringing on Tibetan turquoise and coral beads. My backless embroidered crop top was inlaid with mini mirrors that twinkled in the sunlight. I chose my faded cut-offs, with "Tyke" embroidered in Hindu since they were short enough to show off my slim, brown legs but long enough to remain decent. My ankle bracelets jingled with every step, and my toe rings glittered in the sand. I was ready to party!

Walking the broad width of the beach barefoot, I finally came to a beach house and asked a paler-than-white hippie with long dark hair if he knew anyone on the beach from Ibiza. Without a word, he motioned two houses to the left. I had butterflies doing somersaults in my belly as I knocked softly on the door.

After five minutes, another pale, ashen man opened the door ajar and said, "Yeah?" I said, "Just lookin' for some Ibiza friends who said they'd be here for Christmas." He replied, "Like who?" "Well," I said sheepishly, "Beautiful Barry, Leather Louis, NY Charlie, Soho Angie, and Pasadena Jerry." He snorted and spat into the sand and replied, "NY Charlie is on the beach with Blind Bill," and then he pulled the door closed. I thought there might be at least a smidgen of Christmas décor since Goa was the only Christian state in India.

Toting my flip-flops and bikini in my bag, I walked to the shore and asked a small group of nude sun worshipers if they'd seen Blind Bill and NY Charlie. They pointed a bit further down the beach, and one guy offered, "Hey, you're new to these parts, ain't ya?" "Where ya' sleepin'?" "Dunno, I thought there might be a room to rent near the beach." "Yeah, we got one for $5 a night." "No way, José, I'm lookin' for a freebie or at least a fair shake." "If ya' can't find anything, we can negotiate." They really bummed me out. Man! I was a great catch and probably the coolest chick within miles. They should pay me to brighten up their den!

Spotting NY Charlie by his fair, shoulder-length hair, I yelled, "Hey, Charlie boy, it's Tyke from Ibiza." "Wow, you were serious, ha, can't believe you made it," Charlie shouted in his faded Brooklyn accent. "Man, you look fresh and clean. . . .out-a-sight duds!"

Charlie had a cause. He rejected established institutions, criticized middle-class values, opposed nuclear weapons and the Vietnam War, which he was avoiding in style. He was educated, embraced aspects of

Eastern philosophy, championed love, peace and freedom, was a vegetarian and eco-friendly. Charlie was a true-blue hippie in my book.

There were a lot of hardcore hippies without a cause. You could recognize the cynics, who were ripping off the hippie lifestyle because they had no original generational style of their own. They used the hippie culture as an excuse to consume tons of drugs and stagnate. I was an enigma; I didn't fall into either category or any classification.

"This is my buddy Bill, and Angie's back at our pad cookin' Christmas lunch. Hey, I hope you can join us. Bill is comin' also, ya' gotta come" "Cool, I'd love to!" My self-esteem had rebounded, and I was finally glad to be in Goa. "Hey Angie, you look awesome, super tan and mega groovy in that sari." We embraced with an honest hug, not one of those polite pats on the back hugs for which suspicious women are famous.

Charlie and Angie had a *Finca* (farmhouse) in Ibiza, in the center of the island, near the village of Sta. Gertrudis. They had been living there for the past three years in true, pioneer style. They not only grew their vegetables ecologically, but they also made cheese from their goats' milk, drew water from their well, and lit up their evenings with hand-made candles and oil lanterns. Angie had a butane gas stove/oven and refrigerator, to boot. They were well known for their full-blown, full moon *fiestas*.

The locals in Ibiza were happy as sunshine to rent out their ancestral plantation homes and buy low maintenance apartments in the villages, with the luxury of electricity and running water. However, the earthy farmers, whose roots were planted deep into the rich *tierra*, sold their plantations (often in a state of ruin) but wisely valued their inherited land.

They built themselves a modern chalet on a cleared plot while retaining their almond and olive orchards, as well as their orange and lemon groves. They all had a flock of scraggly sheep, free-range chickens, a few goats, a horse, or mule to plow the field, a hog they fattened to slaughter in the autumn for a winter's supply of spicy sausage, plus half a dozen *Podenco* hounds for rabbit hunting. Charlie and Angie had transplanted their same simple eco-friendly lifestyle in Ibiza to the beaches of Goa, enjoying the warm, lazy winters.

Of course, they liked their evening tokes of weed and chillums of Afghani Gold, but it was always with measured moderation. I was pleased they asked me if I wanted to stay in their guest room until Pasadena Jerry arrived. I figured it would be easy to scout out new digs by then.

It was hard to grasp that I was actually in Goa for Christmas, just as planned nine months ago at the Montesol Café in Ibiza town. I breezed through eleven countries and numerous escapades, but I made it to Goa on time. I congratulated myself for literally floating into Goa on Christmas Day. I had my share of faults, but I was always good for my word. If I said I'd be somewhere, come hell or high water, I was there. Perhaps it was my `Spencer' genes or maybe just my destiny. I was wired to keep my word, so if I give it to someone, they can count on it, Amen.

Angie's Christmas lunch was celestial. Although they were vegetarians, they did eat fish on occasion, and this was one of those special occasions. Exotic fruit salad with lentils to start, followed by steamed bass, garnished with ginger and lime juice, decorated with tiger prawns, created a real tease for our taste buds. Then *pao-baju*, vegetables stewed in hot, spicy coconut-based sauce, served with locally grown short red grain rice. To top off the feast was a typical Goan Christmas cake, *behinca*.

After catching up with news of mutual friends and our various travels, I discovered Blind Bill had complete knowledge on almost every topic. His sinuous, deeply bronzed body and long blond hair offset his pale but piercing blue eyes. Instead of a shirt, he wore Moroccan beads strung on a strip of leather around his neck and knotted an Indian sarong around his slim waist. Bill was an older man, of about forty, and appeared to be very agile for a man without sight.

I diplomatically broached the subject of Bill's agility and that I couldn't detect his blindness. My well-meaning comment was met with laughter. Angie explained that Bill was too vain to wear glasses, especially with his electrifying eyes, so he often fumbled and stumbled around. Bill added, "I've also discovered that lovely ladies want to mother me with my disability, so I play up to it." This northern Californian, who resembled a Biblical character, was sly but amiable and seemed to be on the hippie scene since its inception in 1965. Due to his age and scholarly drug culture wisdom, he was treated as an elder.

* * *

Charlie announced, "Time for a siesta; then we can visit *Rey* Alfonso for a sundowner." They referred to the tall, stately Spaniard as King Alfonso since he was from noble, aristocratic stock. After Alfonso opted out of Madrid's social scene and his eminent duties in the family business, he sailed over to Ibiza in `67 and secured his niche by the ancient walled city. There he started the first island disco. The well-heeled hippies flocked to his club, as he became one of the early hippie entrepreneurs on the isle. His English was fluent, and he instantly had a following.

Some say he started the hippie scene in Goa; others credit `Eight Fingers Eddy.' Alfonso had leadership qualities and an instant following on Calangute Beach. Just before sunset, we strolled over to Alfonso's place, and I was surprised to focus on a mahogany toned male of about six foot four wearing only a bright white loin-cloth. I guess he was an admirer of Mahatma Gandhi, who was obviously a trend-setter. His long, soft curls and huge eyes were as black as coal; he was a formidable apparition.

Charlie introduced me to Alfonso, who graciously lifted my right hand, drew it to his lips without making contact, and pronounced, "Welcome, *Rubi*, to my humble abode." It seemed a bit melodramatic coming from a tall, dark guy, wearing nothing but a large gold hoop earring and a diaper. But, after all, he was holding court. It instantly flashed across my mind that I might become a sacrifice to the gods of his cult-like domain or something bizarre.

About eight other hippies arrived and took their designated places, while the host sat on his throne at the end of the outdoor alcove. I was praying that I didn't have a starring role in the unfolding drama. Everyone sat there in a trance, the calm before the storm.

Alfonso picked up a huge chillum and stuffed it with a ball of black, Afghani Gold hashish. He then cupped his hand over the chillum, placed it between his ring and pinkie finger, and put his mouth over his hand. Using this technique, he avoided the pipe's heated end and created a smoke chamber inside his fist. It helped cool the smoke, as well as catch any embers.

I discovered this was an evening ritual at which Alfonso reigned as King as well as the generous benefactor to his subjects. He had a dramatic finesse that I had never previously seen. All that said, my immediate crisis was how I could avoid the ritual and just pass the peace pipe. I could see I was fourth in line. I looked the part, and peer pressure was squeezing me. I racked my brain, and two excuses surfaced. Thanks, but I have asthma and can't smoke, or I'm detoxing and fasting from drugs.

Either way, I'd look like a wimp or an informer infiltrating the inner circle of Calangute. I decided to fake it. I cupped my hand over the chillum, huffed and puffed without inhaling, then passed the pipe. No one noticed, or they didn't mention it. I always looked stoned, so I didn't have to fake it.

As we were leaving, Alfonso asked me if I wanted to go with him to Panjim the following day since he had to go to the post office and then to the flea market at Anjuna Beach. He had a motorbike. I accepted. Walking back to Charlie and Angie's beach house, I had to fix a point in the distance to focus on so I could walk in a straight line. I had an acute intolerance to all smoke, paint, varnish, bug spray, glue aromas, pesticides, as well as dope. Now I could add Afghani Gold to my long list of - `avoid at all costs.'

Apart from the adverse physical effects, drugs didn't help me with my search for self-awareness. They only made me aware that I despised the feeling that I was in an altered state. Friends told me I had to learn to `go with the flow' and not resist, that I probably had a control issue. Whatever it was, I felt so much better without drugs, or alcohol, for that matter.

It's curious how people try to lay their guilt trip on you. They tried to make me believe that I had deep-rooted problems because I was allergic to drugs. I liked to party, loved to dance, enjoyed communicating, and wanted to have fun, but I needed to find my spiritual grounding above all else. I felt I was getting nearer to my goal. I now realized that all roads possibly led to the one and only supreme power, and I needed a combination of different sub-spiritualities to fill in the gaps. I was quite aware that there were some significant pieces of the puzzle still missing, however. I would continue my relentless search as long as I had breath.

* * *

Alfonso came at 11 am. "Good morning Miss Rubi; you are *muy guapa!*" I was relieved to see he had replaced his loincloth with long, loose trousers and wore a t-shirt that looked reasonably clean. We walked back through the sand to his place to get his motorbike and dragged it up to the road. Alfonso spiked his conversation with superlatives, and I could tell he'd be great in sales of any kind.

He looked like an oversized kid on the *mobylette*. In Ibiza, motorbikes were the primary means of transport. Everyone from fourteen to eighty years had a *mobylette*, which qualified as a runt motorcycle and was a lot faster than a bicycle or horse and cart. There were only a handful of Fiat 500s and two horsepower Citroens on the island, so I had adapted to compact transportation.

We both looked like grasshoppers, with our long skinny legs hiked up to our chins as we sped away. It took us nearly twenty-five minutes to go ten miles, and Alfonso flew around the potholes with expertise. Fortunately, he was unaware that his image as a regal aristocrat and king of the chillum had morphed into a Looney Tunes character. He had a lot of macho self-confidence.

The first stop was the post office. It seemed that Alfonso was sent a monthly check by his older, respectable brother, who took the reins of the family business when their father retired to Biarritz. I think Alfonso was a thorn in his family's dignity, and he was paid off to stay away. The letter had not arrived, and he retreated into a stream of expletives in his native tongue, which sounded a bit menacing.

When he recovered, he told me he'd take me for a tour of the city sights. "But fir-r-r-st, let's have a coffee. Café Baga is just around the cor-r-r-ner, and they have the best *Bolihos de Coco* in town." "Yeah, I'm all for it." I needed a sugar boost every few hours.

I decided I'd better come clean with Alfonso, "I have a confession to make, I didn't inhale the pipe yesterday at your place." "*Si Señorita*, that was obvious. Don't have *vergüenza* (shame); you are *una princesa*." I tried to roll my R's back at Alfonso. "Why, my fr-r-riend, do you say that?" "Oh, I can read people – you've had a *princesa* life of privilege and ease." It was true, but I had broken out of my pampered mold and traveled the world alone on a budget. I was bold, independent, and resourceful. "Oh, I can tell you will need a lot of affirmation, but don't you worry, I can be *un encantador* (a charmer). My words are like kisses of light."

Alfonso was not your usual pot-head, but I could also sense that he was manageable. I was the new girl in town, and he was testing his boundaries. "Hey, why do you call me Rubi, because of my blond streaks?" (Rubia is a female blond). "No, dar-r-r-ling, it is because you remind me of my elegant, beloved Afghan hound, who also had a long nose and lengthy, matted hair." He won me over with that line! Actually, it was true - he had an Afghan hound named Rubi. He always made me laugh at myself. Good therapy.

We sped off in a cloud of dust to take in the sights of `Little Lisbon.' Panjim and Old Goa were magnificent showcases of Portuguese architecture at its best. The first stop was *Basilica of Bom Jesús*, built-in 1594, coinciding with the beginning of Christianity in India. It was the oldest church in Goa and a marvel of baroque architecture. The mortal remains of St. Francis Xavier, the famous Jesuit saint, were a bonus. As we entered, Alfonso splashed his hand into the holy water, made a sign of the cross, and then a half-hearted genuflection. Nevertheless, his deep-rooted faith, or at least respect, was revealed in the church and was very touching. He pointed out particularly important statues, of which one was the Madonna, *la Madre de Jesús*.

Back on the minuscule motorbike, we zoomed past the various temples, the Archbishop's Palace, and Our Lady of the Immaculate Conception, stopping at the Goa State Museum. Alfonso was such a knowledgeable and authoritative guide that a large group of tourists gathered around us. They moved indiscreetly at our pace, hanging on his every word. Weaving our way around the artifacts, I could see my Spaniard was a blatant showman at heart.

"Are you r-r-ready to hit the r-r-road for the Flea Market?" "Yes, siree, do they have food there?" "They have more than everything." After half an hour of dodging chickens, pigs, people, and vehicles, we pulled up to what looked like an oasis. A large grove of date palms created patterned shade, which provided a perfect venue for marketers to sell their artisan wares.

What an intriguingly bizarre patchwork of stuff for sale. Lots of handmade jewelry, loads of drug accessories, drugs, embroidered hats and bags, lots of cool leather pouches and fringed vests and boots, antique silver ankle bracelets, plus backpacks and other travel items. The hippie guys wore loose colorful pajama pants and flimsy sleeveless vests. The ladies wore bikinis or maybe a sarong.

The flea market was the event of the week, and everyone was there. Some vendors were having fun and not in desperate need of making a profit, while others were trying to sell all their worldly possessions to scrape up enough money to get a ticket back home – wherever that was. The locals came to gape at the hippies and looked for faded jeans or other in-demand gear from the West.

I headed for the food, and Alfonso went in search of a new supply of Afghani Gold. Unfortunately, that sought after 'social' drug looked like plump goat droppings and had a rank odor to go along with the appearance. I heard a tale about a guy called Scam Sam, who used to deal hashish on the beach that was cut with heaven-knows-what. He was tarred and feathered and driven, not only out of town but also out of Goa's state.

It was late afternoon and I was ready to head back to Calangute Beach. I needed some space to chill out and reflect on the day. We got back in time for sundowners at Alfonso's den, but I thanked my Spaniard and bowed out politely. He was not offended. I had fun with Alfonso and we became buddies, but he was too old for me. He was at least thirty-eight or more and had signs of aging. I also needed time to keep up with my journal. I wanted to write a book one day about my awe-inspiring travels.

Pasadena Jerry got sidetracked, so I was able to crash at Charlie and Angie's place for as long as I wanted, but I was starting to get itchy. There was a massive chunk of the world I still hadn't seen. I'd met lots of interesting fellow drop-outs but was ready to move on and meet some movers and shakers. Besides, I needed a climate change – it was hot and sticky.

Charlie and Angie convinced me to stay another week until the full moon. They promised I wouldn't regret it since Goa's full moon parties had even better 'vibes' than those in Ibiza. "OK, I have no choice – I'll stay for the mystical soiree." The magnetic field was, without a doubt, altered due to the moon's pull. Just look at the tides during the full moon and the number of births. If the moon has such an effect on the oceans, you can imagine its impact on the fluid inside a pregnant woman's amniotic sac.

9. GOA FULL MOON

It was not just any full moon – it was the Blood Moon in Leo on January 30th, 1972. The sand beneath me was still warm from the sun's intense rays during the day. The drums' soft, steady rhythm produced a trance-provoking backdrop to the mellow, poetic, ethereal tone of the magical flute melody that floated through my mind. It became a melodic mantra that diffused any thoughts that attempted to surface from the depth of my subconscious realm. At that precise moment, an Adonis clone spread his sarong directly in front of mine and whispered, "Shall we engage in silent communication?" I nodded, yes.

He continued, "Let's create a perfect harmony between us. Let's put our mind waves in perfect sync." We stared into each other's third eye, and instantly, we aligned our mental waves into perfect harmony. Two energy rays were emanating from our forehead chakras, each trying to adjust its frequency with the other. Suddenly, a stream of light was formed and became stable; the two-way flow now passed between us. With the speed of a flash, a larger field was created. We were harmonizing our two consciousnesses.

If I had been stoned, I probably would have remained in that mindless state for an indefinite period of time. However, my thought process kicked in, and I became distracted. I could envision the two of us as if I had an out-of-the-body experience. I was peering down at our silent communication, and I started to giggle. I was aware that it wasn't funny, but I couldn't stop laughing. I guess I punctured the atmosphere. Adonis stood up and dragged his sarong to the nearest lady insight to have another go at silent communication.

Meanwhile, the drum rhythms abruptly changed to a 'get up and dance' tempo. Two or three more bongos joined in, creating an authentic African beat. To dance deep-African properly, you had to know how to shake a tail feather while rotating your hips and mix in some exaggerated high stomping without losing the rhythm. Then you had to throw in a few wild pirouettes, followed by spinning your neck repeatedly in full circles, allowing your hair to keep the momentum going.

Before long, I heard applause encouraging me to continue. Then Kwame, the cool French dude, joined me and we danced up a storm. He was born in Senegal, so the beat belonged to him. We almost ignited a fire from the friction of our feet on the fine-grained sand. Other dancers backed off and gave us space. He mimicked my every move, and then he took the lead, and I followed him. We were dubbed the dynamite dancin' duo. We danced until the drums ebbed and then ended up in the sea to cool off.

Kwame invited me over to his nest of friends for a toke, but I explained I was on a weed fast, and he was perplexed but impressed. His lady didn't look impressed with me at all, so I was relieved when a long, golden-haired guy introduced himself. "Hi, I'm Luke from Ohio, and I just want to tell you that exhibition was the most original dancing I've ever seen." I thought, yeah, from Ohio, you probably do square dancing or the polka.

"Hi there, I'm Marie France from New Orleans." "Ahh," replied Luke, "That explains it." "Explains what?" "I've always heard that New Orleans was the birthplace of jazz, as well as the home of a Creole voodoo queen." "Yeah, that's how the story goes." Luke asked, "So how did you get here?" I gave Luke a brief resume of my travels thus far and explained that I was on a spiritual journey. I then threw the ball back into his court.

"How did you get here?" Luke described his silk route journey that started from Munich with another American guy. They took the overland route in a VW bus through Turkey, Iran, Afghanistan and Pakistan to New Delhi, then south to Goa. "Wow, but you still look so fresh and well-scrubbed, almost luminous. How did you manage to remain so unscathed from the effects of that brutal route?"

"Possibly because I don't do drugs, for health reasons," Luke admitted. "Well, whatever you have, it certainly doesn't show. You look like a poster boy for vitamin pills." "No, I'm not sick; it's just that my system rejects all drugs." "Awesome, that's the same with me," I interjected. Luke looked sincerely interested, "Tell me about your spiritual journey." What an opportunity I had to enlighten this middle-America hippie-of-sorts. I was able to tell him about the merits of Tibetan Buddhism, Sikhism, Hinduism and Yoga!

"How about you, Luke? Aren't you curious to know if there's a higher power?" "I know the higher power; I'm a disciple of Jesus." "What a coincidence; I'm a fan of his also. He rates as one of my top prophets and teachers. Gandhi was also a follower of Jesus, but he got burned out with Christians 'cause they wouldn't let him into church due to his color and caste. But don't you have a guru, I queried?" "My guru is the Holy Spirit," responded Luke.

I whispered, "Cool." Luke admitted that he studied the Holy Scriptures and the Dead Sea Scrolls. He told me that the Holy Spirit had given him a verse for me. I felt exceptional and waited patiently for him to write it out on an index card. Peace enveloped Luke's words as he read, "Ask, and it shall be given to you; SEEK and ye shall find; knock and it shall be opened unto you." Mat. 7:7

I couldn't believe my ears; those poetic words resounded into the depths of my being, "I can't believe it, Luke. That verse is straight from heaven. How could you know those were the exact words my soul craved?" I simply stared at Luke in disbelief. He just smiled a clean, wholesome smile. His teeth were Hollywood perfect and glistened as he spoke. He was a gentle guy, different from anyone I had met on my travels so far: no hippie jargon, but a profound insight of genuine spirituality without alternative motives.

"It was great meeting you, Marie France - keep dancing and keep searching." "I will." I wanted to know WHAT made Luke tick; he had such a serene presence. He possessed something I needed. I'd have to zero in and investigate more about his prophet, Jesus.

What also impressed me was Luke's lack of ulterior motives. He was not trying to sell me anything: no healings, no fortune-telling or an encounter, no self-awareness course, no yoga class or magic rocks, or even protective oils. He had no slick agenda to catch a girl off-guard. How refreshing! He seemed almost angelic. Perhaps Luke was an angel. I believe my higher power is protecting me and always has. Yeah, something I wanted to follow up on.

It was about 3 am when Charlie and Angie asked if I was going back with them or if I'd make my own way home. "Yep, I'm ready to go." They teased me the whole way back, "First we saw you in a trance with Kyle, the self-appointed guru of Calangute, then Mr. Personality, Kwane, followed by Luke, the Jesus Freak. Hey, did he convert you?" "He didn't try to; he gave me a verse from the Holy Scriptures that was written precisely for me. It was like he could read my soul, and the Holy Spirit inspired the verse. Luke seems well connected. He said the Holy Spirit would lead me into all Truth. I thought he was a cool guy, ten-out-of-ten."

Angie insisted on throwing me a farewell soirée and wanted to know who she should invite. "Awesome, you two will go down in history as the best ever, let's see, Luke absolutely, Alfonso and the sundowner crew, of course, Kwame and the French clique, and Kyle, why not? Also invite Blind Bill, Mariah, Tamara, Bamboo Bob, Dippy Dave and the rest of the musicians, and of course whoever y'all wanna ask."

Angie said she'd cook a big pot of spicy vegetarian vindaloo, and everyone else could bring a snack or side dish, plus their drinks and drugs. She glanced over at me with a smile and asked, "Banana split for dessert?"

"Absolutely," I grinned. "I'll supply all the bananas, chocolate sauce, local cashew nuts, grated coconut, and the ingredients for your homemade ice cream." "Okay," laughed Angie, "What flavors?" "You choose, but your vanilla, chocolate and strawberry are awesome." "It's your party, so that's what you'll get." Charlie and Angie were ready to host a party at the drop of a hat.

My sentiments about leaving Goa were mixed. My time there was a vibrant lesson on the hippie hierarchy. The pecking order of freaks was based on commitment and lifestyle; the longer your hair, the thinner you were, the more rings and beads you wore, the more embroidered your clothes were, the more you looked the part, the better rating you received on the flower power social scale. I could hold my own, but what was the point - to become the most far-out drop-out? Yep, it was time to move on.

Charlie and Angie's fete was super-cool. I wore my Balinese scarves artistically. The electrifying colors complemented one another. I cleverly wrapped one scarf around my waist and looped two others over the waistband so that glimpses of my leg showed when I walked or danced. Another scarf I twisted into a backless halter that emphasized my deep tan. After all, the party was in my honor, and I wanted to shine! As parties go, that was definitely their thing, their claim to fame in the community. Charlie and Angie were kind, and they loved to please.

I often wondered if altruism existed since people who love to give selflessly obviously receive a boomerang effect of self-satisfaction. Or does sacrificial giving really exist? I mean giving, without any emotional, physical, or spiritual satisfaction in return. Something I would contemplate. . . . later.

Once again, there were the hugs, the *namastes,* and promises of reconnecting again at a later date or in another life. I was embracing the legitimate lifestyle labeled nomad-ism. The accepted cycle was Ibiza, Formentera, and Morocco in the spring, Kabul and Kashmire or Bali in late summer, and Goa in fall and winter. Most of the regulars at Calangute

Beach were flagrantly adhering to that merry-go-round cycle of going everywhere, yet nowhere.

I wanted to pay the full month's rent for Charlie and Angie's beach house, but they refused. Nor would they allow me to pay half. So I decided to give Angie the antique silver belt I bargained myself breathless for in New Delhi. It was my prized possession, so I figured it was rated as sacrificial giving, and I felt pleased with myself for that.

Angie gave me a special piece of crystal that I had often admired. She convinced me that the prismatic stone would promote good energy flow and rid my body and mind of any negative vibrations.

She said, "Historically speaking, crystals are touted as ancient forms of medicine, with philosophies borrowed from Hinduism and Buddhism. The benefits are amazing." She added, "Just holding crystals or placing them on your body will activate physical, emotional, and spiritual healing by interacting positively with your body's energy fields. This crystal will even help balance your chakra points, improving your concentration and creativity."

"Awesome, I'll try sleeping with that miracle gem under my pillow." I wasn't totally convinced but would give it a try. I had read an article that `healing crystals' were mined in places like Burma and the Democratic Republic of Congo, where mineral extraction is linked to severe human rights violations and environmental harm. Even seven-year-old children work in the cobalt and copper mines, where covetable "healing stones" such as citrine and smoky quartz are mined. I hoped my crystal had not promoted that type of exploitation.

It was accepted and expected that everyone would exchange little mementos upon departure. Of all the unique, global gifts I received, my most treasured gift was the poem Luke gave me, etched into a piece of parchment. I would miss this communal living, with all its eccentricities, but there's a time and place for everything under the sun, and my time in Goa was done.

* * *

There was a local bus leaving from Calangute to Dabolim International Airport every four hours, so I figured if I went on the 8 am bus, I'd be at the airport with plenty of time to catch the flight to New Delhi at 11 am. There were only a few other foreigners on the bus, but no one I knew. The bus stopped twice to let people off and on, and a local lady of about thirty-five, wearing a sari, came and sat next to me. (There were other vacant seats, so I guess she wasn't afraid of catching lice from a hippie.) She wore her hair in a neat single braid that extended to her waist, and she had a delicate, tiny nose stud. The red *bindi* dot, painted between her eyes, signified she was married or engaged.

"How do you do? My name is Lavana. What is your name?" "Hi, I'm Marie France from the United States. Are you a visitor here also, or do you live in Goa?" The petite lady replied quite seriously, "I am born here and 100% Konkani." "Uh-huh, what is Konkani exactly?" "Konkani is an ethnolinguistic group resulting from the assimilation of the Indo-Aryan, Dravidian, Indo-Portuguese, and Austro-Asiatic ethnic and linguistic culture."

I thought, what a mouthful to explain Konkani, I shouldn't have asked. "Ahh, sounds like a great mix. Where did you learn to speak English so well?" Lavana replied matter-of-factly, "In Wales." "You mean Wales, in the United Kingdom," I asked? "Yes, my English professor's father was from Wales, and he insisted I spend my summers there to perfect my accent."

After a month of mono-syllable conversation, using hippie jargon, I was finding it a challenge to follow Lavana. I was fascinated by her education in Goa. "So, did you go to school here in Goa?" "Yes," she replied, "I went to CPIR." "What kind of school is that?" "CPIR stands for Center of Post Graduate Instruction and Research. The University of Bombay established it in 1961." "Cool," no wonder she was so articulate and a downright show-off.

Lavana continued, "I thought it would be interesting to speak with you and find out what brought you to Goa. Do you take drugs?" I adored the naïve directness of the Indians, no beating around the bush. "No," I confessed, "I don't take drugs; I don't even drink alcohol." Lavana raised her eyebrows, looking puzzled, "Then why did you come to Goa?"

"I'm on a spiritual-type journey and heard that India was a good place to experience enlightenment." I added, "I understand that Goa is basically Catholic." "Yes, there was a Portuguese Inquisition in 1560 established to enforce Catholic Orthodoxy in the Indian dominions of the Portuguese Empires and finally abolished in 1820." Again I was at a loss for words, "Oh, I'm sorry to hear that. I've heard that Inquisitions were so unfair and quite dangerous." Lavana laughed, "That is an understatement, anyway it happened many years ago, and I have no hard feelings. My ancestors are Hindu and fortunately escaped the Inquisition."

"I'm learning about Hinduism, and I've been doing Yoga for several years now." "Well, perhaps I was led by Brahman to sit here so I could better inform you about our beliefs." "Yeah," I smiled eagerly, "That's exactly what I was thinking." Actually, I was telling a white lie; I found this lady uppity and a bit of a know-it-all.

"Well," explained Lavana, "Many people mistakenly believe that Hindus worship thousands of different gods; however, we worship one Supreme Being called Brahman, though he has many other names. This is because India's people, having multi-languages and cultures, have a different perspective of God.

"Supreme God has vast divine powers. When God is formless, He is referred to by the term Brahman. When God has form, He is referred to by the name Paramatma. We Hindus believe that God has three main forms; Brahman, the creator above all, Vishnu, the sustainer, and Shiva, the one who destroys."

Lavana added, "Hindus believe in many gods who perform different tasks: like executives in a large company. These gods should not be misunderstood as the Supreme God. "The unique insight into Hinduism is that God is not far away, living in a distant heaven but is inside each soul, in the heart and consciousness, just waiting to be perceived. And the goal of Hinduism is to know God in this intimate and experiential way."

"Wow, I didn't realize that, Lavana. I thought you Hindus believed in at least ten thousand separate gods. You've thrown some light my way." Maybe this little Indian lady knew what she was talking about after all. She sounded like a school teacher.

Lavana continued, "Hinduism gives the freedom to approach God in one's own way, encouraging a diversity of ways, not demanding unity in just one way. It permits people to believe in and pray to their own concepts of the Divine, in whatever form they choose. There is no demand for allegiance and no punishment for lack of belief, yet there is provision for wisdom, comfort, compassion, and freedom to those who seek it."

It sounded like a `win-win' philosophy to me. "Amazing" was all I could muster, "It'll take me a while to get my head around that `far out' belief system and digest such a wide-angle lens of liberty. It is so comforting to hear about a religion contrary to `one size fits all.' I like the way it leaves space for individuality."

On the other hand, I wondered if freedom could be valued without bookends of boundaries. However, it did seem to fit my dimensions of rebellion to the established norms. I needed time to let it filter and sink in alongside my other revelations. But, wait a minute, what about the wretched caste system and the untouchables? They had no hope of ever ascending to a higher position in life. There were still a lot of loopholes in this belief system called Hinduism.

Lavana smiled, "Are you aware that you are speaking with an Indian accent? I find it very charming, coming from a foreigner." Without any conscious effort, I responded to people in a parrot-like fashion. The problem was, I didn't want to offend my bus companion by telling her I was probably mimicking her accent. I feigned disbelief, "You don't say! It must have rubbed off on me in the months I've been traveling around India. I'm sure it will disappear when I get back home."

In New York, I sounded like a Brooklyn Jewess. In New Orleans, I had four accents; Cajun, uptown, downtown, and back-of-town. In Texas, I had an unmistakable drawl. In Mississippi, I spoke red-neck dialect, and in Tennessee, I had a hillbilly accent, and so forth. After Transcendental Meditation, I concluded; I was a parrot in a previous life. I bobbed my head like a parrot and even walked a bit pigeon-toed.

By now, we were approaching the airport, so I thanked Lavana for taking the time to enlighten me. As the terminal came into view, I started to daydream about Rajasthan and the mystique of the vibrant, multicolored markets and the famous palaces and infamous forts. I could visualize the nomads, in full regalia, performing the snake dance to the tune of their hypnotic trance music.

As we went our separate ways, I waved to Lavana, wished her well, and then skipped to my Air India check-in counter for New Delhi. I found that skipping gave me acceleration and promoted blood circulation. I desperately needed some blood in and around my brain after nearly a month of vegetating in the serene surroundings of Goa.

Fortune was on my side once again. There was a fantastic exhibit of antique airplanes on display on the runway. I wondered if they were from the 30s or '40s. They looked like the planes from World War II films. My flight was called on time, and I looked forward to a ‘chill-out’ flight to New Delhi before facing the tumultuous train station. The rail ride to Jaipur, the Pink Capital of Rajasthan, would take another five hours.

* * *

I felt like Amelia Earhart as I entered the twin-engine propeller-driven Douglas DC-3 aircraft, and it suddenly clicked why my ticket was so cheap. The antique aircraft I admired from afar proved to be Air India's national fleet. I wondered if we would be assigned parachutes, or at least leather flying helmets and goggles.

Wouldn't you know it, a big, plump, sticky looking man plunked down in the seat next to me with several bags of food. I guess he knew that in-flight meals were not an option. Oh well, I'd think positive and make the best of it. This was luxury travel compared to riding a camel or an elephant from Goa to Jaipur, as they did in days of yore.

His first course was something that smelled like goat's cheese, followed by a pungent curry dish, which he shared generously with me by way of indiscreet burps, diffused by the propeller's loud hum. I congratulated myself for having the foresight of purchasing some peanuts and a giant chocolate bar at the airport. Still, I would wait until the aromas emitted through my neighbor's pores began to subside. Mr. Plump's large head kept flopping forward, and I prayed it wouldn't roll over onto my bony shoulder and crack my collar bone.

I rejoiced to discover that Mr. Plump slowly drifted into a motionless coma, and I was able to enjoy the rest of my bumpy ride in the World War II relic, feeling like a heroine returning from a successful mission over enemy territory.

I spent the next several hours scribbling down Lavana's info on Hinduism while it was still freshly bouncing around my brain. I would also reflect on the philosophy and doctrine of that ancient religion, plus the reality of how it was being lived out. I'd hang onto the good parts and toss out the rest. Amen.

When the plane touched down in New Delhi, I leaped over Mr. Plump with my lanky stride to exit as quickly as possible. I needed to find my way to the train station and the platform for Jaipur by 4 pm, or I'd have to wait until the night train. I psyched myself up for the fierce assault on my senses from an onslaught of hectic travelers, but at least now I knew how to locate the jam-packed path to the ticket office and the platforms.

* * *

I stuffed wads of paper into my ears to block out the screeching roar and warning blasts of the trains coming and going. I then reverted to the comfort zone of my happy childhood memories at Union Train Station in New Orleans. For many years, I waited for "The Panama Limited," with excited anticipation, alongside my mom and brother (the favored child), to pull into its slot and zip us off to paradise.

Every summer, while my dad spent his required month at National Guard Army Camp, the three of us escaped to Wisconsin, avoiding the tropical heat, mosquitoes, and thunderstorms. I remembered back to the happy year of 1954 when I was seven. I wore a tailor-made straight skirt and matching fitted jacket with a brown beret and a similar toned shoulder bag. People dressed up in those days for travel, and I looked like an afro Barbie doll with my dark tan and frizzy hair.

I proudly wore my favorite lacy socks, but my clunky saddle oxford shoes killed the Barbie doll 'look' and accentuated the size of my feet. Those huge two-tone orthopedic shoes made my skinny legs appear as if I had been a victim of polio. Of course, they were advised by a well-meaning, licensed podiatrist. I was one of the smallest in my second-grade class; nevertheless, my large hands and feet were a tell-tale sign of my future stature, just like puppies with big paws, I guess.

We lucked out; our sleeping car was named Pelican, the Louisiana state bird, as well as my favorite feathered fishing friend. Our private sleeping compartment had bunk beds, plus a Murphy, drop-down-on-command type bed. I vividly remember drifting to sleep with the comforting, hypnotic click click – click click of the wheels resonating on the tracks. I would have sugary dreams of our cool, idyllic destination - Janesville, Wisconsin.

My Aunt Charlotte and Uncle Jerry had a large home with a manicured lawn that extended down to Rock River, where we would go fishing. My aunt and uncle spoiled us rotten, but my summers there had given me refuge and an emotional hiding place to return to during the storms of life. For example, when I had my heart set on my very own pink Volkswagen Beetle, my dad insisted on a big baby-blue Buick that looked like a tank. I was fifteen and wanted a flirty, cute car, but my dad exerted his authority, and I drove around town in an armored vehicle, which I found so humiliating.

"The last call for Jaipur"… … yikes, the porter was lifting the steps as I ran screaming at the top of my lungs, "Wait for me, I'm a diplomat!" I don't know if he believed me, but the train waited. I hurdled up the steps, the porter blew his whistle, and off we went.

Ingenuity and futuristic hope were on display at that rambunctious Delhi station. An attractive free service was provided for that city that was literally bursting at the seams. Men could get a free vasectomy and a Coca-Cola in the privacy of the main terminal, with sheets separating each ongoing operation. Bring a friend and get a coke was the `come on' throw-in bonus.

Finally, I had some down-time. The train car was only half full, and as we sped out of New Delhi, I took a deep breath and audibly sighed. The tension from the train station drained from me, "*om padi padme hum, om padi padme hum.*" My Buddhist serenity mantra was just what I needed. After about ten more minutes of my peace mantra, I started to doze off when suddenly a post-puberty Indian rocker walked thru the car with a ghetto blaster. I had seen lots of locals clinging to transistor radios as they strut through the streets of Delhi and Bombay, proudly showing off their portable music machines. But portable tape decks were hot off the US press, so I was astonished to see and hear one in my tranquil train car in India.

Due to this gigantic nation's immense overcrowding, silence was not an accepted part of the culture. It was absolutely not an option. There was no room for silence. I prayed that `Boy Pop' would keep on walking to the next car; however, some prayers go unanswered. He sat down, not far from me, with his "blaster" balanced on his knees. I suppose he moved from car to car to share his great portable sound system with us, deprived passengers.

The problem with typical pop music from India, female singers had voices ranging from high C to high, high C and you got a sore throat only listening to the love ballads backed by nerve-wracking, unknown instruments of auditory torture. I was contemplating getting up and huffing away with a look of disdain, when. . . .whoa, Led Zeppelin's biggest hit, composed by Page and sung by Plant, came floating out of the speakers in waves that caressed my senses. It was my all-time favorite song of the year, and I had seen the group `live' in the funky Warehouse concert arena in New Orleans about a year ago. I knew all the lyrics of "Stairway to Heaven" and sang along with passion.

I could picture Robert Plant shaking his long, thick curls and Jimmy Page in full strum, with his double-neck Gibson guitar, screaming out melodies I could never forget. Hallelujah, `Boy Pop' had some of the top hits from the UK and USA sandwiched in with the local Indian talent.

Plopping back down in my seat, I started knocking my ring on the armrest and tapping my foot. I was tempted to get up and dance, but that might look undistinguished for a diplomat. Hey, yeah, "American Woman" by The Guess Who, and then "Oh Happy Day" by the Hawkin Singers. Tears began to well up in my eyes, and I was startled to realize something in the song was hitting a raw nerve in my soul - I started to weep.

Trying to feign composure, I questioned the phenomenon that was occurring. I was pretty much of a control freak and prided myself on not displaying my emotions. The English part of my heritage, I suppose. But my outburst was something I had to deal with at some point. Perhaps I needed some inner healing or more self-awareness. But never mind, I'd think about it later. Inwardly I sighed, echoing Scarlett O'Hara, "After all, `tomorrow is another day.'" That is the way we southern belles were wired, and that's how we coped.

Needing to circulate my blood, I walked back and forth through the ten swaying cars several times, mixing the rhythm of my stride with short skips for cardio, pogo jumps for the leg ligaments and prevention of clots, plus some ballet stretches between cars on the platforms. By the time I finished eating my *chole bhature* (fried, baseball-shaped bread) with some spicy chickpeas, I felt fit as a fiddle and was ready for an introduction to Jaipur, The Pink City.

I was traveling light, so I would be super mobile to jump off the train, into a rickshaw, and onto the streets. After a month and a half in India, I was convinced it was a super-safe country. After all, New Orleans had the highest violent crime rate, per capita, in the entire US. Because the Crescent City was off the charts on the yearly crime index, I grew up street smart, as far as detecting tell-tale signs of a crime about to happen so I could sprint in the opposite direction.

I wasn't paranoid because that was the only life I knew, but now I could appreciate the exhilarating freedom of walking around day or night without any worry of aggression. I didn't even need pepper spray. Wowee! I wondered if the fear of *Karma's* consequences kept the Hindu men in line. (Their worst fear must have been to fail their *Karma* exam and end up as a woman in their next life.)

10. JAIPUR

I descended the train with optimism. I knew from experience to grab the biggest, toughest looking kid to escort me to a rickshaw taxi. He would fend off his mass of rivals and pick up his tip from the taxi driver. Thus, I would be spared haggling over transport prices while being swamped by a dozen wild children.

Mariah, the dope accessory vendor in Goa's flea market, gave me a good tip for a historic hotel in Jaipur's old city, near the best bazaar. I went straight to the Khatu Haveli (old house) Hotel. The price was right, and the room was reasonably clean, so I took it on the spot.

Like the homes in Andalucía, Spain, this Old House Hotel of three hundred years was built around an inner courtyard, which allowed light to illuminate the rooms. However, colored glass was used in the windows facing the courtyard, so you always had a sickly green, yellow, or blue complexion. But hey, you can't have it all - the ceilings were high, and it didn't smell too musty. The big plus was the solitude that accompanied the inner rooms.

Venturing out into the night with a merry heart, I was eager to discover a new city. Jaipur was just short of 700,000 inhabitants. It was a fifth the size of New Delhi and a tenth of the population of Bombay. However, there was also a ceaseless activity. People were pushing carts, selling cigarettes, hawking imitations of everything, trying to lead you to their brother's carpet shop, horns were tooting, and there were swarms of begging boys.

Applying the same tactic I used in New Delhi - I asked the receptionist in my hotel. He recommended one of his hotel boys named *Divit*, which is the Hindu word for `immortal.' It sounded like a safe choice. I knew the receptionist would siphon off some of Divit's earnings, but that's how it was.

What delicious street food! I ate some curried vegetables and rice from a street vendor and a bottled drink. Curry was a stand-by since it burned up the bacteria and disguised any rotten flavors. By now, it was 10 pm, and I would call it a day and start early the next morning. I had an appointment with Divit at 9 am.

I woke up singing, then picked up Divit at the desk and hit the noisy streets with high spirits. I was so proud of my wise decision to bow to the protection, pay-off fee, and enjoy the sights of Jaipur without being hassled at every turn with having to negotiate rickshaw charges. Divit also knew the bus routes.

The first stop was Hawa Mahal, referred to as the `Palace of the Winds.' This architectural wonder, built with pink/red sandstone in 1800, boasted nearly a thousand windows. The beautifully carved, honeycomb-shaped windows had a dual purpose. They allowed the breeze to blow through the palace, cooling it off, and also permitted the royal ladies to watch the daily drama in the street below without being noticed.

The Hindu kings of yesteryear had many princess wives to ensure that they would not be attacked by the particular kingdom each wife represented. So it seems that many of the wives were political decoys, while others genuinely won the king's heart and affection.

The Pink City, Jaipur, actually received its nickname when the Prince of Wales and Queen Victoria visited India in 1876. As "pink" denoted the color of hospitality – Maharaja Ram Singh painted the whole city pink. Therefore, it seems clear that the Indians were people-pleasers and anxious to win favor with the British regime. And actually, the British Military was not as standoffish and uppity as imagined since many returned to the United Kingdom with beautiful Indian wives.

Jal Mahal was next on my list of imperative `must-sees' in the Pink City. It was six miles from the center, but Divit said it was easy to take the number five bus that went directly there. He was such a respectful young man of about seventeen and treated me like royalty. I decided to try and fit into the culture and wore my wild hair in a single neat braid. Also, pulling my hair back revealed the five gold hoops in my left ear, demonstrating my approval of Indian ladies' ear décor. "Do as the natives do" had become my slogan.

However, there was nothing I could have done to look less foreign. If I had worn a sari, I might have resembled a drag queen instead of an Indian maiden. My unisex figure even defied lady's trousers back home. The surplus hip and thigh fabric made the pants resemble poorly designed jodhpurs on me. I shopped in the men's department to get the leg length and lack of hip. I was long-legged and high waisted. With only a mere eight inches from my waist to my armpits, I had atypical proportions. How fortunate!

Jal Mahal, built in the 17th Century, is a salmon/red-toned, historical palace in the middle of the man-made *Sagar* Lake. It is therefore called the Water Palace. Divit explained there were rowboats to rent if I wanted to paddle around the palace, but I could not enter for safety reasons. I'd rowed boats and canoes most of my youth, so that was a breeze.

I chose a lovely pink rowboat and told Divit to hop in, but he couldn't swim and probably didn't trust my boating skills. I had a vigorous row around the palace and was tempted to jump in the lake for a swim, but wasn't sure if I could pull myself back into the boat. I hadn't tested my arm muscles lately.

My brother was a great personal trainer. We water-skied, since we were nine and ten, on the languid rivers of Louisiana. By age fourteen, he was a superb speed-boat skipper and got a kick out of pulling my featherweight around. Just when I had the velocity to jump the wakes with style, he would slow the motor, so I'd start to sink, and at the point of no return, he would then full throttle the powerful motor so that I could learn the sensation of flying. The only drawback, my biceps still bulge due to hanging onto the ski rope to avoid the poisonous Water Moccasins.

Starved from all the exercise, I needed calories immediately. Divit knew of a small family-run vegetarian restaurant not too far away. We headed there at a fast clip, and within eight minutes, I was stuffing my face with *naan* bread, hot out of a *tandoori* oven and drizzled with yogurt and mint dip. Then we were served a mouth-watering *Dal* (Indian lentil curry over rice), followed by *Til Patti* - a famous crispy dessert birthed in Jaipur. It was a first-class meal for pennies.

There was a fort nearby, perched on a hill overlooking Jaipur. Elephant rides were offered for a rip-off price due to the inaccessible vehicle route to the lofty fort. We hoofed it with ease. After several hours of inspecting every nook and cranny of Amber Fort, we headed back down the hill and caught a bus back to the city, then a rickshaw to the hotel.

Divit was very efficient and knew the ropes. I was clearly not his first tourist, nor would I be his last. I didn't consider his inquisitiveness as intrusive since I understood the Indian psyche and their curiosity about everything. They dreamed of a better life in lands of opportunity, where they could shake off their caste limitations and follow their hopes of superseding their present circumstances.

Divit was lightning fast, and each time I paid in rupees, he would tell me the equivalent in dollars, pounds, and German marks. His young mind was already competing with calculators and computers. He insisted that personal computers and handheld mobile phones were just around the corner. I thought, "dream big, my boy," and chuckled under my breath.

Back at the hotel, I took a refreshing shower. Even though there was no pressure and the water looked rusty, it was wet. I always carried a bar of soap with me, in a custom made, plastic case, as well as a roll of toilet paper. Neither luxury was supplied at hotels or restaurants. I mean, not to complain, it was a huge step up from camping or sleeping in a VW Van! As far as I was concerned, I felt blessed.

* * *

Now to fulfill the main reason I came to Rajasthan and, in particular, Jaipur. I knew it was where I could find the antique silver tribal jewelry with which I had fallen in love. Not only did I want to purchase some prestige items for myself, but I wanted to set up contacts for future purchases. I knew there was a market in the West for these ethnic treasures.

My goal in life would remain the same; to be a traveler and a seeker. I needed to fund that obsessive drug that had taken hold of me in its addictive grasp. "Is there more to life than this?" I would keep traveling and keep searching until I found the answer. Without a work permit in Europe and no desire to be an employee, I knew I would have to live by my wits, and I wanted to enjoy the trip along the way.

It was 5 pm and I had a full, satisfying day taking in the sights and sounds of Jaipur and the surrounding areas. I decided to skim through Bapu Bazaar, then zero in on a strategic attack the following morning. I went alone since all the vendors spoke English, and I couldn't afford to have the prices hiked up to accommodate a cut for Divit.

The Bazaar was everything I had hoped for and more. It was so jam-packed; I had to focus, with selective vision, not to become swamped with input. There were tons of jewelry and gemstones since Rajasthan was the hub of the jewelry industry. The fabrics were celebrated, and everyone wanted spices from Jaipur.

Spotting only a few antique silver tribal belts and other silver jewelry, I pretended to be nonchalant to keep the price down. The Indians, who could afford it, bought quality, hand-crafted gold jewelry. Ethnic tribal jewelry was the last thing they were after.

I was in the right place at the right time. The ethnic, bohemian `look' was about to explode onto the fashion scene, and I wanted to be well prepared with the authentic goods. I had a nose for what would sell and followed my intuition.

The nomadic tribes of India make up nearly sixty million of its population. These tribes belong to the lowest step of the socio-culture and socio-economic ladder. They mainly originate from The Great Thar Desert of Rajasthan, located in northwest India. The vast arid wasteland covers nearly eighty thousand square miles and forms a natural boundary between India and Pakistan.

These desert inhabitants live haphazard lives and, to this day, roam about on camels, which often pull carts filled with their meager belongings. Some are shepherds, others subsistence farmers, while a large handful live from the sale or trade of cobra's venom. The snake seekers belong to the tribe called Kalbelia. They are also known as Saperas, a gypsy caste. Of all the nomads, the Kalbelias are by far the most colorful and resourceful.

The cobras can spit their poison up to a yard in hopes of blinding their offenders, and their bites are fatal. Meanwhile, Kalbelia men and their young sons comb the desert, alert to the snakes' favorite hiding places. With a long staff, they fling enormous cobras into the air, and upon impact with the sand, they skillfully grasp the back of their necks, rendering the cobras helpless, and stuff them into a sack and carry on the search.

I'd heard that the famous "Snake Dance" of the Kalbelia women was the most entertaining, sensuous, athletic, and mesmerizing dance in all of India and beyond. Their dazzling, colorful outfits and sparkling silver jewelry make them royalty in the desert, and more recently, given them a budding career in the pricy hotels of Jaipur. I would definitely take in a show or two before leaving town.

I awoke early with the excitement of returning to the Bapu Bazaar and would investigate the stunning silver belts I had previously spotted. I entered the Bazaar, turned the corner, and scanned the shop, but the belt was not there. I was horrified that I didn't snap it up on the spot, for any price.

I tried to appear cool and bored and poked around at some gaudy, gold jewelry and casually asked the merchant if he happened to have any silver necklaces or belts. I said I had seen an old beat-up silver belt the previous evening. He reached into a white cloth bag and pulled out the belt. "Something like this, mum?" I replied without enthusiasm, "Yeah, more or less like that." My heart was racing, but I took a few deep breaths and continued, "I have a friend in London with a shop, and she's looking for a wholesale outlet for old silver stuff." I would try the "wholesale" tactic. "I want to buy a sample to bring her, and if it's what she wants, I'll be back for a big order."

The merchant's eyes lit up while his head bobbed left to right and back again as if it was attached to his body by a spring. "I have more mum, but they are at home. The people who shop at Bapu mum want quality gold jewelry. If you come with me to my home, my wife will fix you some authentic Jaipur food, and you can see what a nomad left me last week." I jumped at the chance, "Well, that fits in with my plans today, so I'll take you up on the offer." It never crossed my mind that this smallish, thin man could have any ulterior motives. I automatically counted on his karma to keep him in line.

The vendor was innovative, as all Indians are. He said his brother would start his shift in a few hours so that he would be free at noon. I agreed and skipped away, knowing that I had just encountered another fortunate stroke of good fortune.

I was back at twelve on the dot, and Mr. Anand introduced me to his look-a-like brother, then we headed to the nearest bus stop. Although he was a head shorter than I was and possibly ten pounds lighter, he seemed quite okay with being seen with a foreign apparition as weird looking as I was.

Not one person glanced at my wild hair, which cascaded past my derriere and resembled the knotted carpets sold in the market. Neither did they notice the antique ivory bangles stacked from my wrists up to my elbows. The bi-standers didn't seem to care that I wore Moroccan embroidered trousers, with the crotch that dropped to my knees and then tightened at my ankles - but short enough to show off my jangling ankle bracelets. For a bit of class, I wore a silver Lingam pendant over my mirrored tunic. I later discovered that the Lingam stone was seen as a symbol of energy and potentiality. It was better known as a fertility stone—what a dangerous piece of jewelry!

After a twenty-minute bus ride with multiple stops, we arrived in a somewhat shabby neighborhood, and Mr. Anand proudly led me up the steps to his fourth-floor apartment. He was part of the budding new middle class of Indian. For centuries upon centuries, there had been only three economic strata - the wealthy, the poor, and the destitute.

Mr. Anand's wife looked only slightly surprised. I supposed that I had not been the first foreigner he had brought to their humble dwelling. His wife greeted me with *"Namaste"* and kindly showed me in. The proud merchant pointed to the electric bulbs hanging from the ceiling, then led me to their kitchen sink and turned on the water. He grinned with fulfillment and announced, "Water and electricity."

Returning his smile, I confirmed, "You are a very fortunate man and a good provider for your family." Anand told me that his two teenage children were at school and excelling in their studies. I believed him. In the far corner of the room was an altar with offerings of what looked like a glass of water, fruit, flowers, and incense. I was aware that it was proper for a Hindu to worship at home, as well as in temples.

It seemed that we would eat first before I could see Anand's stash of silver jewelry. I was thankful since I was experiencing a sugar drop and needed a quick fix. There was a large mat on the floor, and Mrs. Anand gracefully placed two large platters on the mat and waited until her husband sat down on the floor first, then looked at me, so I followed suit. She sat down gracefully, arranging her sari in a single swoosh.

I was pleased that Angie, back in Goa, had explained to me "eating etiquette" just in case I was ever invited into an Indian's home. The cross-legged position in which people sit to eat food served on the floor is called Sukhasana, which helps apply pressure to the spine, facilitating relaxation. Sitting in a relaxed position allows you to concentrate on the food's taste, texture, and quantity.

While eating in that posture, you also move back and forth, helping your abdomen secrete the required digestive juices to assist digestion. I was glad Charlie, Angie and I had often eaten on the floor, Indian style. I certainly did not want to commit a *faux pas,* so I studied their every move and waited for the head of the house to start. I could have woofed down the entire meal for three but went slowly, in case there was no refill.

Mr. Anand asked, "I hope you are fond of India food, mum?" "Oh yes," I replied, "It is my preferred food in the entire world." (Perhaps I exaggerated.) "*Dal-baati-churma* is the specialty here in Jaipur; I hope you like it. My wife is an excellent cook, and that is why I married her." His wife blushed as her gaze shifted downwards, but I could tell she felt it was a backhanded compliment.

"My wife's *Dal* is made with a combination of five types of lentils. The Bati (small wheat bread balls), dipped in pure *ghee,* (clarified butter) is the best." I wondered if I could lick my fingers between dips and swipes or just let the goo residue drip onto their nice, clean mat. I hoped I would get the timing right with my rocking so that my digestive juices would get the message to start producing enzymes.

I congratulated myself on not making a mess and following the guidelines correctly. The only drawback, I was still famished, and no re-fills were forthcoming. But Mr. Anand remained in a seated position, so perhaps there was more to come. "My wife's *Churma* is fit for the gods." I hoped *churma* was edible. The Mrs. of the house removed the two plates and delivered a brown mound with lumps. I was ecstatic when I discov-ered the mound was similar to American fruit cake. I had three slices.

Mr. and Mrs. were civil to one another, but I could feel an undercur-rent of discord. I knew that Indian women were treated as second class

citizens at best and slaves at worst. Many were victims of domestic violence. Mr. Anand's wife probably had an upbringing that prevented her
from questioning her spouse or her in-laws. Yes, there was a dark side to
Mr. Anand, and I picked up on a master-slave element in his marital relationship.

Mr. Anand disappeared for five minutes and returned with three
white cloth bags and laid them gingerly on the only table. He extracted
one spectacular belt after the other while I tried to remain aloof. Meanwhile, my inner-being was screaming, YES, I want them all....NOW. I
wanted to wear them all at the same time. I wondered if I had an obsessive disorder. I calmly asked the prices. Anand studied each code, making
quick calculations, and came up with a price.

These `maiden belts' were all handcrafted. The thick silver cord
wrapped around the maidens' waists was made up of ten to twenty heavy
silver threads, woven together for strength while remaining totally flexi-
ble. They were snake-like.

The buckles were then glued to the woven silver rope with resin, fas-
tened together by an ornate screw that slipped through the small
merging loops from each side of the buckle and screwed into a silver bolt
at the bottom.

I knew I could sell the belts for perhaps eight to ten times the price I
paid, and I'm sure Mr. Anand had the same markup. Therefore it was the
poor nomads that got screwed. I suspected that Mr. Anand's ancestors
were from nomadic stock, and he broke the mold by setting up shop in
Bapu Baazar. He told me he could obtain an unlimited supply. Ta-da! I
was in business!

This tribal jewelry would be my ticket to future travels, as well as my
trademark in ostentatious accessories. What I lacked in beauty, I compensated with an overall eye-catching presence. That is the trickery of the
French, especially in Paris. They know how to put themselves together.
That is the definition of style. Either you have it or you don't. You can't
learn it, and you can't buy it.

On the other hand, I had considered the possibility that my eclectic collection of clothes, hats, and accessories might be a subconscious effort to compensate for past insecurities or low self-esteem. I also considered the possibility of a full-blown identity crisis, but I'd think about that some other time. After all, "Tomorrow is another day."

I decided on two silver tribal belts as my samples, from which I could take orders. I would return to Jaipur on a bi-annual trip for a big purchase of silver, as well as fabrics and gemstones. My American Express traveler's checks were a significant wedge in bargaining but dwindling rapidly. Everyone wanted dollars. I would buy more traveler's checks in New Delhi and charge it to my parent's Golden American Express card. I still had a small reserve of cash in my US account, leftover from the sale of my car and furniture.

After all, I had contacts with "in" shops in Rome where I could sell my wares, and if my Jewish girlfriend, Rise, had true prophetic gifts, I would be modeling. Several sources of income would keep me traveling in style. I decided I had a nomadic streak within my DNA. I couldn't bear it if two days were the same. Change produces a stimulus, and I realize that the only thing constant is change.

Mr. Anand was polite but not overwhelmed with my purchase. The sparkle in his eyes dimmed, without blacking out. I gave him my business card, my mom's Art Gallery, and he brightened up again. He believed I'd be back, and so did I. I thanked Mrs. Anand for her hospitality and allowed Mr. Anand to escort me back to Bapu Bazaar by bus.

On the ride back, he cocked his head and enquired, "What is your purpose in life, mum?" I couldn't believe lightning would strike twice in the same place. The Sikh on the airplane already asked me that question. I sighed and said, "I am on a spiritual journey." He paused and replied, "Is that to justify your aimless travel, or are you really looking for the Truth, mum?"

"Oh yes, I am looking for the Truth." "And if you find the Truth, will you follow it?" I thought a few seconds, "Of course I will." "But, even if there is a cost, a commitment, or a sacrifice?" He had me stumped; I thought I would. "I hope so," was my reply. Indians could easily overstep their boundaries, but I knew their culture did not allow them space to be subtle. People talked about the big questions in life and not just the weather or other trivia.

* * *

When I got back to my hotel, I went directly to the reception to enquire if the Kabelia dancers were performing in the city, perhaps at a pricy hotel. He made a phone call and replied, "Yes, mum, the Cobra Gypsies are booked at the Hotel Oberoi each weekend." It was Saturday night, so I asked the receptionist to reserve me a ticket. "Sorry, mum, they are booked up."

I was desperate, "Tell them I'm a journalist, and I want to write a story about their hotel and the dancers." He related my request - there was a three-minute pause, then the answer was transformed into, "Yes, in that case, you can come at 9 pm". I didn't want to puncture my Karma, so I decided to write an article anyway and present it somewhere.

"Whoopee!" I still had time to eat, freshen up, and change to my flashy crop top to display one of my new maiden belts on my tanned, bare midriff. I chose the belt with the biggest buckle but was tempted to wear them both. I took some of my mom's business cards that said, Adventures in Art. That just might work. I was writing for a travel magazine called 'Adventures in Art.' Why not? I would give my mother a copy of my article and retain a clean conscience.

I arrived twenty minutes early to locate the performance hall and introduce myself to the manager. I discovered that Indians were trusting and quite used to wealthy foreigners looking eccentric. They led me to a front table, and I could see that the night club was already filled. There were quite a few other hippies in the audience. The lights dimmed, and the master of ceremonies announced, "Put your hands together for the Kalbelia Dancers, who hail from Thar Desert. They will be performing the "Cobra Dance" for us tonight."

I remembered Darcy, the young French lady who I'd met at the full moon party in Goa. She told me she had taken lessons from the Kalbelia dancers in Jaipur, who'd set up camp on the outskirts of town. They had traded in their camels for colorful wooden trailers and became semi-city dwellers. The men had become tinkers and traders, while the ladies danced their traditional Cobra Dance on the streets and in the hotels.

Darcy had taken lessons for a month and told me that I'd pick it up immediately. As you might have noticed, the word "gypped" is a derivation from gypsies. It is no coincidence. However, their dancing and music were worth more than any asking price.

There were ten people on the stage, including the musicians. Among them were five female dancers of different dimensions and ages, two male dancers, and three musicians. I had never seen such cartwheels of colors celebrating a dance of any kind.

The ladies all wore full, circular skirts weighted down with hand embroidery, mirrors, shells and gold ribbon, falling into rich folds. Surprisingly enough, the skirts were still light enough to twirl and fly up, exposing strong legs covered in bright hand-knitted stockings. Their tops were a snug fit with a burst of color topped off by electric hued headdress-scarves that began at the hairline with tassels and extended to their waist.

The men wore multi-hued turbans that screamed florescent colors, while the musicians were more subdued but masters of folk music. They genetically inherited the art of playing the Pungi, the wind instrument used to charm snakes. It is a flute made from cane reeds and stuck onto gourds with beeswax, and the perfect backdrop for the dancers to strut their stuff with snake-like movements. The combination of an animal skinned drum with small cymbals, a homemade stringed instrument, and castanets kept the rhythm pulsating.

As the music started, the ladies, one by one, outmaneuvered each other with an extraordinary exhibit of their specialty. One nimble, seasoned lady was an expert twirler. She remained on a fixed point and made full 360º revolutions up to ten or fifteen times, with her full skirt flying, trying to catch up with her. I wondered if she might drill a hole in the floor, producing a gusher of oil.

They all moved their hips in a gyrating, circular motion, resembling that of a writhing serpent. Simultaneously, they moved their arms while turning their wrists with a circular flow, and their fingers opened and closed gracefully - similar to the Spanish gypsies dancing the flamenco.

A few had the gymnastic ability to perform a slow, controlled backbend while shimmying their way backward until their head touched the floor. Then they tucked their head inwards, grasping a ring from the floor with their teeth, and worked back upwards with Olympian abdomen and back muscles. This was no ordinary folk dance; this was pure art and pure entertainment at its best.

There was wild applause and even a standing ovation. As hotel shows do, they invited audience participation for the following dance. I remembered in Ibiza, a Spanish guy once told me, "The English tourists take the bait each time, and make fools of themselves by trying to do the flamenco dance gracefully. You must be born with those genes to capture the rhythm and attitude, or else you'll look as awkward as a cow on ice."

Well, I got the point. However, this was different - I knew I could mime the snake dance well enough to try. I had the advantage of being the backbend princess in our gymnastics class, plus pirouettes were my specialty. I had studied the dancers' every move, wanting to replicate that snake dance at the next full moon party.

I stepped up onto the stage with another lady, perhaps in her thirties. She had the advantage of being dressed similar to the dancers. Maybe she was one of the students, doing a bit of PR for the nomads' school of tribal dance. The way I looked at it, I couldn't lose. I would have fun, practice for the next occasion, and provide something else for my book one day.

Quickly unscrewing the bolt fastening my gorgeous silver belt, I laid the treasure onto the edge of the stage. My lightning-quick mind warned me that the heavy buckle might knock my two front teeth out when I leaned over backward to touch my head to the floor. The belt couldn't slip down, but it would glide over my small, aristocratic bosom and wreak havoc on my large teeth, straightened meticulously in my pre-teen years with stainless steel braces.

The music began, and I nodded for my dance companion to have the first go. That way, I had more time to study her moves and try to outdo them. She had the advantage of a full, circular shirt that enhanced the momentum of the twirling.

I just thanked my lucky stars that I wasn't wearing jeans that evening. At least my Moroccan style pants were non-restrictive. They had enough elastic in the low, embroidered waistband to allow me to move freely, without allowing too much exposure. My signature moves included gyrating, shimmying, and of course, pirouettes. I moved with the music while she danced, practicing my arm, wrist, and finger movements that I had learned in Spain.

First, I waited until the applause for my dance companion subsided. Breathing deeply, I repeated my mantra and called upon my deities as the spotlight centered me in its blinding brilliance. I could feel the music as I entered into a rhythmic oscillation. I could see a dancer placing a ring, on edge, in the strategic spot I could aim to reach. I became the dance; it took over. I tried to obey and keep up with it. I whirled endlessly, gyrating like a belly dancer, maintaining my arm, wrist, hand, and finger movements. I shimmied as if I had motors embedded in my shoulders and controlled my backbend while I continued to shimmy. The only thing I missed was grasping the ring with my teeth because my nose knocked it flat to the floor.

"Shucks!" I was made of rubber, but my nose was too long. Nevertheless, I had an amazing workout; I loved to dance! My adrenaline was still pumping when the cheering crowd stood up. No, they weren't leaving; they were giving me a standing ovation. "*Olé!*" I basked in the approval. I was a people pleaser, and I needed affirmation – just as Alfonso had perceived back in Goa. I bowed a few times, working the crowd, then picked up my belt and returned to my table.

A man in a suit sat down at my table and introduced himself as the manager. He complimented me on my tribal dancing and whispered, "Well, mum, you are more than a journalist." I handed him my business card, "Adventures in Art." He quizzed me on the dates of the publication of my upcoming article. I explained it all depended on what stories were scheduled ahead of mine. I took his card and told him I would advise him as soon as I knew the dates. "Also, the Kalbelia dancers want to know where you took lessons since they don't know you, and this is their territory."

After centuries of begging food and risking their lives extracting cobra venom, the Kalbelia Gypsy Tribe finally traded snakes for dance and music. The tribe was prospering, so I understood their suspicion of someone moving in on their territory. Women, who were finally lifted up out of slavery and placed on pedestals due to their unique dancing talent, did not tolerate competition.

I understood and snuck out into the night, hailed an auto-rickshaw, and high-tailed it back to my hotel. I could have never persuaded them that my performance was a first attempt at the snake dance and that I had not taken lessons from their competitors. I regretted being such a show-off, but I was still working on learning how to fade into the background, without much success.

Nevertheless, I continued to relate to the gypsies and their nomadic lifestyle. It was intriguing how they managed to maintain their customs, language, and way of life throughout the centuries. The largest mass of gypsies left Rajasthan, India, in a single migratory wave, as early as the 11th century. They left because of the caste system, droughts, and famines. As they poured out of northwest India into Turkey, Romania, Bulgaria, Hungry and Spain, their origin was believed to have been from Egypt; thus, they were given the erroneous nickname of Gypsy.

Once settled in the Balkans and a majority within Spain, they often referred to themselves as Roma rather than Gypsies. I can understand their allergic reaction to a demeaning nickname that became a slur and an insult. However, now the Kalbelia tribe held their heads high, as they had received international acclaim and were basking in the limelight. Their high cheekbones, large eyes, and even features endowed them with a mysterious dark beauty that was amplified when they danced.

As for me, it was time to move on. I still had so much of the world to see! I checked out the train schedules for New Delhi and chose the 11 am express to get me into the capital by 3 pm. I was eager to experience Kashmir and the houseboat hotels in Srinagar after the rave reviews I heard while in Goa. Luckily I managed to find a flight on Air India from New Delhi to Srinagar. By 7:30 pm, I'd be touching down in the Kashmir valley and ready to explore new territory.

11. KASHMIR – HOUSEBOAT

As I stepped out of the plane, I was hit by a sharp cold gale, a wake-up slap welcoming me to Srinagar, the capital of Kashmir. Never one to research places I was traveling to, I preferred a surprise. I jogged across the tarmac to the airport terminal to work up some body heat since I was only wearing my trusty bell-bottoms and a short sleeve cotton t-shirt. Oops, I guess that's why everyone headed to cool Kashmir during the heat of August! I preferred doing things out of order, despising routine. I opened up my carry-on sack and pulled out my three t-shirts and four scarves to bundle up.

It was early spring in Kashmir, and I felt fortunate to be in an invigorating climate and was glad to discover I was the only foreigner on the plane. Of course, that should have been an alert signal that I was traveling during the off-season. Never mind, I would have Srinagar all to myself, yippee! I saw a mass of humanity moving together towards me in a large clump, and the roar got louder as I neared. I could distinguish shrill voices, "Taxi? Houseboat? Rupees! *Baksheesh!*" I relied on past experiences and grabbed the tallest, strongest boy in the crowd. He shushed the clamor and whisked me to a waiting taxi.

"I'd like to go to a houseboat hotel, that's not too expensive." We drove around Dal Lake until I yelled, "Stop!" Then I'd jump out, inspect the boat and haggle for a week's stay. I finally chose a houseboat after a five-minute debate. The taxi pulled away, and I realized I had forgotten to ask if there was heating.

Never mind, I saw a hot water bottle lying on the side table next to the bed and was relieved to know at least there was hot water. I wondered if I could rent or buy a goat to sleep on my bed. I'd heard that the Kashmiri goats' down was incredibly dense and warm. On the other hand, I could buy a cashmere sweater and have the bed to myself. I'd heard that each boat came with a servant.

"Good evening, mum, my name is Abdul Ali. You want supper, mum?" I nearly jumped out of my skin. There was a hulking apparition standing in the shadows the entire time I jumped on the bed, flushed the toilet, turned on the tap, and flickered the lights. After all, I needed to see if everything was in working order. "Ah yes, what's the choice?" "No choice, mum, today is *goshtaba* with rice." The system was you ate whatever the family ate in the houseboat moored next door. I was famished, so whatever *goshtaba* was, I was sure I would like it.

I whipped the blanket off the bed and wrapped it around my shoulders in squaw fashion. When Abdul lit the candle on the dining table, I had to stifle a gasp. He looked like the fulfillment of a Hollywood make-up artist's dream. He resembled a human being transformed into another dimension through long hours of make-up artistry. Abdul was the spitting image of Quasimodo from the hunchback of Notre Dame Fame. Well, you can't read a book by its cover. Quasimodo was a very kind, tender person.

Abdul served the *goshtaba* piping hot with rice. He said, "We call this the `King's meal.'" It consisted of ten small, rounded balls that resembled the leftovers from the King's eunuchs' transformation. On the other hand, they might be mutton's eyeballs. I was into eating what the locals ate, so I took courage and cut a ball in half, only to discover it was a grey, mini meatball. I took a bite, and it was delicious. The mini balls had been simmered in yogurt gravy with special spices. Abdul told me it was minced mutton, and I made an "m-m-m-m" noise.

Abdul was trying to be attentive. Every time I took a sip of water, he refilled my glass. I got up the nerve to say, "That will be all for this evening, Abdul." But he remained two feet away, staring at me. So I repeated with sign language, and he sat down in a nearby chair. I said quite bluntly, "Good-bye Abdul," and he carried away my empty dish, licked clean.

Phew, I'd had a long day, with the train from Jaipur, and then flying from New Delhi - so I relished the silence. I had a low tolerance for high decibels and was content in the chilly solitude of my damp boat. I did my breathing exercises for twenty minutes. Breathing in peace and love 2-3-4 and breathing out negativity 2-3-4. I exhaled the hectic Delhi train station, as well as the helter-skelter Srinagar airport. Amen. My thoughts wandered over the beauty and treasures I would soon uncover. I drifted off into a sweet sleep. . . . .

With nearly transparent curtains, I awoke with the first rays of the sun and belted out, "Let the sunshine. . . ." I arrived in the dark of the night, so when I gazed out the window, BOOM, I was smacked with a close-up view of the snow-covered Pir Panjal mountain range, jutting majestically towards heaven. I did not doubt for a second that God was our supreme creator because his fingerprints were everywhere.

I slept in layers of everything I owned and started to peel off as my boat warmed up. There was a knock at my door, and Abdul asked if I wanted breakfast. "Yes, please, what is it?" *Nunchai* (salt tea) with *chapati* (flatbread) made of rice. An egg is extra." "Great, I'll have all that with two eggs."

My mom was a breakfast martyr. She always woke up at 5 am and needed to do something. So after gardening, she started making Crèpes Suzette. Instead of the standard fluffy pancakes, we preferred a stack of paper-thin crepes to roll up with grape jam oozing out and powdered with sugar. She prepared fried eggs for an encore, sunny side up, bacon or sausage, doused with maple syrup. Blue cheese and grits were optional. So I always woke up hungry. The strange thing was. I had "hollow legs." I never filled up and never filled out. I longed for some dangerous curves, to no avail. After a string of tests, doctors deemed I had a fast metabolism and would remain a string bean.

The owner of my boat kindly offered to take me on a tour of Dal Lake with his *shikara* (long skiff boat). My tour would start at 10 am, so I had time for my Sun Salutations, some meditation, plus chakra channeling. Mid Yoga, a boat pulled up overflowing with flowers. I wondered if I had woken up in Shangri-la. Then another skiff laden with fruit moored, so I bought a selection of organic fruit. The next boat was filled with carpets, but my boat owner shouted something at them, and they left.

This was a dog-eat-dog world. I was the only tourist in Kashmir with thousands of merchants after my meager stash of rupees. But, my personally assigned angels had protected me so far; therefore, I had every reason to believe they were still on duty.

My houseboat owner, Mr. Fawaz, moored his colorful, hand-decorated *shikara* and helped me gingerly into his craft. He wore the typical *Karakul* cap that was brimless, an unstructured version of the Shriner's fez, but without the tassel. His long, loose gown reached past his knees and covered his low-crotched trousers.

Deciding on my comfy white trousers with a blue T-shirt for a nautical look, I hiked my hair up into a ponytail as the best tactic to keep my frizzy locks from blocking my view in the breeze. I then wound one scarf around my neck and used another as a shawl. I hoped to find a locally embroidered, warm shawl in an attempt to defy the afternoon deep-chill.

I felt at home on a boat. Louisiana's license plates read, "Fisherman's Paradise." Fishing was my Dad's number one hobby, so we followed suit. With our fishing camp, just across Mississippi's border, we naturally made it our weekend mecca. Some of my favorite sibling photos are of my brother and me in our own little fishing boat. It was a cute eight-footer with a two horsepower motor manned by my brother.

In the earliest photos, I was wearing a diaper. I questioned my mother, and she said, "Oh honey, you both had on life jackets, plus you both knew how to swim." We were two and three years old! I dared not ask more but wondered if our whining and fighting had driven our parents to the brink when they'd pushed us offshore in that little boat. That way, they could have some peace and quiet and try to recapture their sanity.

As I looked out onto the snow-dusted, towering mountains surrounding me and drew the clean, pristine air into my lungs, I couldn't help but belt out that old hit, "I'm in heaven......" Mr. Fawaz broke into my tune to tell me about the history of Kashmir. Perhaps he had been a tour guide or a school teacher.

"The first Muslim Ruler of Kashmir was in 1320." He babbled on about Bulbul Shah, the Sultan, who converted to Islam, and then he skipped a chunk of history and continued. "The Mughals (Turk and Mongol Tribes) reigned here from 1580 to 1750. During this era, successive Mughal emperors landscaped the famous gardens and mosques plus ornate palaces were constructed. I will be pointing out some of the gardens shortly."

I thought, wow, a free sightseeing tour. Mr. Fawaz pulled close to the shore so I could see a magnificent garden with a man-made waterfall and an unusual variety of imported trees that were still going strong after hundreds of years. I uttered sounds of amazement.

I realized the majority of inhabitants in Kashmir were Muslim. It was obvious. There was a different vibe with Muslims - they lacked the laid back tolerance of Buddhists and Hindus. I could feel the same aura that I felt in Morocco. The people seemed more abrasive, and there was a specific hostile element. Oh well, variety is the spice of life; every culture has its pros and cons. Mr. Fawaz pulled to shore again and told me he would take me on a tour of a carpet factory. I thought, how very kind of my landlord to take me on such a thorough tour of his fair lake.

We walked up a path that led to a gargantuan wooden warehouse that had a slant to it. It obviously had a faulty foundation. We were greeted by three men who resembled the Three Stooges, but with deep tans and skull caps. They jumped to attention and, with smirky smiles, chirped, "Welcome to Kashmir, we are the best and cheapest carpet factory in all of Kashmir."

Returning their contrived smile, I realized they were after my Yankee dollar. I wasn't in the market for a silk carpet or any carpet but thought I should respond politely. In about three minutes, they had unfurled at least twenty carpets, with a single flick of their wrists, occasionally knocking each other in the head. I started saying softly, thank you, but I don't need to see more. They kept unrolling more and more carpets until I screamed, "STOP!"

Within five seconds, everyone disappeared, like magic. I thought I must have said "stop" with more authority than I had planned. I waited a few minutes, then started wandering around and saw several overhead light bulbs swinging and some rugs sliding off the shelves. I ventured outside to see if I could find the disappearing act. They were standing about fifty yards from the building in a huddle. I thought, maybe it's their morning tea break, and they dashed out for their caffeine boost, or perhaps it was their prayer time.

Muslims were very punctual with their prayer routine, five times a day on their prayer mat, facing the holy city of Mecca. I shouted, "What's up?" "EARTHQUAKE, mum. We must stay far from the building, mum." I thought to myself, "Those weasels didn't tell me to run!" I did feel a small vibration, though.

I had never experienced an earthquake. It didn't feel severe, but the men refused to return to the building. I was relieved that the tour was cut short. Mr. Fawaz leaped back into the boat and said it would be safer to visit the floating market. He had the sense to ask me if I was interested in buying anything. I replied, "Yes, actually, I'm looking for a warm but lightweight cashmere shawl.

His eyes brightened as he explained that cashmere was made from the downy under fleece of the *Changthangi* goat. "Cashmere is one of the most sought after commodities in the world. The hair fiber is softer, lighter, and up to three times more insulating than sheep's wool."

He explained that the goats are found in Outer Mongolia and Tibet, and the downy undercoat is collected once a year. The preparation is tedious, so the best quality can be expensive. The cheaper grade of cashmere usually has yak hair or rat fur mixed in. I chuckled to myself and figured this guy must have graduated `Cum Laude'` with a degree in goat hair!

We pulled up to a parked houseboat, and Fawaz shouted something. A thin man appeared with a small face and huge eyes, wearing a skull cap and carrying about ten shawls. He sprung onto our boat like a frog and demanded, "Feel the quality, mum, feel the quality."

"Yep, really soft," I admitted. He then produced what looked like a wedding ring and pulled two yards of wide shawl through the ring with one smooth continuous yank. He looked at me with such a need for approval that I felt literally obliged to applaud!

Haggling for at least six minutes, I settled for a steel blue wrap that would complement my jeans. His sales pitch was that the goat hair from which my shawl was made came from the Gobi Desert that stretched from northern China to Inner Mongolia. Usually, I'd visit a bunch of shops before making such a pivotal decision, but I was getting chilly. Anyway, I'd re-sell it when I got back to Europe and repeat the Gobi Desert story.

It was nearly noon, and I wondered how Fawaz would slot in his prayer ritual. I knew that Muslims were devout and never missed their five-times-a-day prayer sessions. I often quizzed my Iranian pal back at LSU (Louisiana State University) when we had coffee breaks together. We became friends because neither of us fit into the `WASP' mold; since we had that in common, we bonded as mutual outcasts. I was curious if he had a set formula for his prayers.

Mohammed explained that first, he did a ritual cleaning, then a four-step pattern consisting of praising God, asking for forgiveness, praying for blessings, thanking God, and chanting Amen. He emphasized that Muslims believed in only one supreme God, creator of all and above all. Although they called their god *Allah*, he had ninety-nine names revealing all his attributes. I told him, "Well, Mo, (I always gave people nicknames) that sounds pretty parallel to the pattern our church taught, laid out in The Lord's Prayer."

There was so much strife between religions when all along, there were a lot of similarities. Mo offered to give me a copy of the Quran, which the Muslims believe to be the direct revelation of God's codes and laws. This was revealed to the Prophet Muhammad in the 7th century AD. He said they believed in Jesus as the penultimate prophet and messenger of God. I exclaimed, "Well, why all the hoopla and dissension? Amen!" Perhaps I'd have time to read the Quran, to give the Muslim's beliefs a fair shake. I'd include a review of the Quran to round out my investigation and search for The Truth.

Mr. Farwaz asked me if I'd like to eat back at The Lucky Flower, my houseboat, or have something at one of the dinky dining skiffs in the float market. I opted for a meal in the market. Knowing he barely had time to speed home for his noon prayers, I was glad to have a break from his monotonous history lectures anyway!

I had to walk over a floating barrel bridge, balancing my big bowl of fruit. I gobbled it down using my right hand and motioned for a refill. With fifteen minutes before Farwaz returned, I did my ballet stretch exercises and performed a few *jetés*, ballet leaps, to check on my flexibility. Ah, that felt sublime. I'd do my full-blown yoga routine when I got back to my houseboat.

Farwaz returned punctually and motioned to me to get into the boat, but I played hard-to-get and kept leaping around until his eyes narrowed, and I knew he meant business. I jumped into the boat, and he whizzed me off to a copper factory.

Explaining to Farwaz that I had nil space to carry back a copper bowl or sculpture, he nevertheless insisted. I guess we had to make the rounds to his immediate family's enterprises before he'd set me free. After all, transportation was complimentary.

We moored at the copper factory, and two men greeted us with copper items in their hands and under their arms. No one dared to enter their shops or warehouses due to the aftershocks of the earthquake. I asked if they had something small in copper, and they came up with two thimbles, so I couldn't refuse. The first sale of the day is considered "good luck," so they put up with my shenanigans to open the way for more profitable sales.

I could tell Farwaz was not going to be deterred from his full factory tour. Off to his cousin's *Papier Mâché* shop. There were ancient gardens along the way, so nothing was lost, and I sat back and enjoyed the cruise. I decided to strike up a deal with my landlord, "Mr. Farwaz, I'll buy something from the next place if you let me row back." I was aware that Muslim men thought women were born to be bossed around.

I could hold my own at arm wrestling, thanks to my brother's strict training. This exercise entailed my clasping his right wrist firmly with both hands and pushing his arm away from my body as hard as I could. He wisely discerned that aiming a dagger towards my chest would give me more incentive to push away even harder. It worked! It was a reliable form of "extreme isometrics" and was also good for my pectoral muscles.

Mr. Farwaz laughed, then sneered, "This boat is much heavier than it appears, and your skinny arms, mum, will never have enough power." I responded, "Is it a deal or not?" He finally agreed, "Yes, if you buy a gift at my cousin's shop." I browsed around a while and chose the cheapest thing I saw, a paper mâché bangle.

I leaped into the rear of the boat and sat down in the driver's seat. I then grasped the long, heart-shaped paddle with both hands and dipped deeply into the mirror-smooth lake and pulled—three strokes on the left side, then over to the right, three strokes. I kept the boat in a steady, straight direction by repeating that pattern with the help of my power mantra; "*om-mani-padme-hum* . . . .la-la-la."

Yes, the paddle was much heavier than the oars I was used to back home, but hey, I could use both arms for just one paddle. "Easy-peasy!"

I was hoping that lots of Farwaz's friends or acquaintances witnessed the switch in gender roles. Now I was the boss. Farwaz was impressed that my upper limbs had such power since he was unaware of my years of hanging onto a ski rope and pushing a dagger away from my vital organs. I wanted to show my landlord that I was not a pushover; however, I didn't want to lose his favor completely or humiliate him too much. "Phew, I've had enough," I faked. "Thirty minutes is enough for me."

Farwaz beamed and told me to pull over to the next dock, and he would take over. I was eager to experience the wholesale float market at daybreak the following day, so I needed to stay on his good side. "I've heard the biggest event on Dal Lake is the morning produce market, and I would love to see that." "Well, for a small fee, I can take you since I need to buy some fresh vegetables anyway." I murmured under my breath, "Right-on!"

Daybreak was 5:24 am, so I'd have to rise by 5 am. I went through my intricate, full-blown yoga routine, read my book on positive thinking and drifted off to sleep early.

"Breakfast, mum," Abdul boomed, staring at me from the dining room. "Good, you can just put it down and leave," I replied, in hopes that he would disappear like a genie, back into his bottle.

Dawn quickly shook off the darkness, revealing forty to fifty low-riding wooden boats in the distance with men perched on the bows and maneuvering around each other single-handedly with a paddle. My guide was punctual.

Mr. Farwaz started his morning lecture, "The market's produce comes from the `floating gardens' that fill large swathes of Dal Lake and around the market. They are made by weaving together roots and twigs into a floating mesh. On this base, farmers add layers of cut weeds, algae and silt to a depth of five feet, stretching up to four-hundred feet in width. They leave narrow waterways between the floating gardens for the vendors to maneuver their way around."

"How fascinating," I replied, not listening to his babbling. "Look, look," I pointed through the chilly haze to the flurry of activity taking place in the near distance. The shallow long skiffs looked as if they'd sink under the weight of the organic carrots, turnips, radish and collard greens. This was the wholesale market, not the housewives' browse about market. Prices were being debated, and deals being closed. It was the commodities market of the waterways.

He then paddled to the floating shops to show me his brother's saffron and flower store. Pointing out his brother's houseboat (the Lotus), he explained that this was the nearest end of the lake to Srinagar's old city. "Oh, great! I'd like to have a look at the old town. It's supposed to be the Venice of the East." Farwaz's face grew solemn, and he sternly warned me that it was a dangerous city with pick-pockets and worse. I didn't believe a word of it, but I wasn't in the position to stage a mutiny. I would sneak into town later.

It was yet another day's captivity to Farwaz's agenda. He paddled me to six more outlets around the lake, sandwiched between his five devotional prayer slots. I knew I would have to plan an escape. I tried to remember the details of Papillon's break-out from Devil's Island. Ah yes, he strung coconuts together to form a raft. No coconuts in Kashmir, so I decided to borrow Farwaz's *shikara* to paddle myself to freedom. I had paid three nights in advance for my houseboat, with breakfast included, and had the receipt. I wanted to do everything as legal as possible for my karma's sake.

My great escape was at 3 am in the still of the night. Silently I crept into the skiff, and then I pushed it out into the lake and let it drift for about ten minutes before using the paddle. I couldn't risk even the sound of a ripple. The moon was almost full, so I had plenty of light to find my way to his brother's house, where I would moor the craft.

I left a polite note on my bed explaining where he could find his boat and a nice tip for Abdul. My heart raced with excitement since there was an element of danger involved in all this. I located Mr. Farwaz's brother's houseboat after a twenty-minute search. There it was, "The Lotus." I silently tied up the boat, tip-toed to the main road, then headed towards the city lights. I alternated between fast walking and jogging to stay warm.

12. SRINAGAR

This was my first glimpse of Srinagar after three days of captivity. I breathed in the frosty air and thanked my guardian angel for his/her faithfulness. "Hallelujah, mission accomplished!" I pulled my shawl up over my head and walked through the empty streets on the lookout for lodging.

I rang the bell next to the locked door of the "Happy Hotel." After three rings, a man half asleep opened the door and said, "Yes, what you want, mum?" I answered, "A room, isn't this a hotel?" "Yes, mum, but can you come back at 8 am?" "No, do you want me to report you to the Better Business Bureau?" "No, mum, enter; why you come in middle of night?" I told a white lie, "Night flight." "Oh, follow me." He took a key from a drawer, and I followed him up two flights of steps with my heavy bag. "I will get sheets and blanket, mum."

The room was nothing to write home about, but I could always find another hotel after a good night's sleep. I was out in a flash and didn't mind the sagging mattress or the hard pillow. After all, tomorrow is another day.

Feeling energized, I awoke raring to go. Finally, I would have a new city to discover with more markets to sift through. I was FREE. I sang with total abandon, "Born Free." There was a knock at the door, and someone yelled, hey, I'm trying to sleep, so I hummed the rest of the blockbuster melody within my heart.

I did my Sun Salutations with oomph, jumped into my jeans, layered myself in T-shirts and wore my cashmere shawl, Muslim style, draped over my head, hanging down past my waist. On the way out, I told the sleepy receptionist that I needed a better mattress and pillow, or I'd have to look for another hotel.

It's incredible the results I got when I spoke with a bit of stern authority. I thought the best way to get my bearings would be a slow rickshaw ride around the old city, which would allow me to remain aloof and out of reach from the merchants' sticky hands, dragging me into their shops - Moroccan style. Muslim shopkeepers had a more aggressive approach than the Buddhists and Hindu merchants.

I chose my bicycle rickshaw driver and was surprised that a group of screaming kids didn't tackle me. I guess, being early season, the boys were still wandering around the city, forming into groups. I chose a turbaned sprite man who was apparently Hindu. He wore a long wool tunic and baggy trousers to the knee and looked raring to go.

Whenever I saw an interesting shop, I announced "STOP" and climbed down and investigated the wares. I had my guard up because I knew the percentage trick from New Delhi. Arjun warned me that bystanders would try to walk into the shops behind me to claim they led me there and claim 10%. I was on the lookout.

At least four lakes crisscrossed by ancient waterways and intersected by the Jhelum River coiled through the city center like a serpent. Srinagar probably had more miles of canals than streets. I was enthralled to be back in a city, able to wheel-and-deal, my favorite pastime.

First, I wanted to delve into the Jamia Masjid Mosque. It was the most surreal place in the city, with its ornate Indo-Mongol architecture and spectacular courtyard with hundreds of wooden pillars. I was spellbound by the quantity of Friday worshipers that turned up and their steadfast devotion to *Allah*.

Just across the street from the mosque was the bustling market of Lal *Chowk* (bazaar). I paid my cycle driver double for his trouble and told him I'd spend the day in the bazaar. I felt like a kid in a candy shop, I wanted one of everything, but I knew I needed to stay focused on my mission. I wanted to make contacts for the future when I returned on buying trips. I needed to fund more travels.

Due to the British Empire's presence for two-hundred years, English had remained the mainstay language for communication, especially among tourist shops. After a few hours of scouring the stalls, I returned to the best shop with antique, hand-embroidered, hand-woven, cashmere shawls. The items were nearly half the price of those Mr. Farwaz has shown me on his monopoly tour of Dal Lake.

As I entered the shop, a man was on my heels. I was fed up with the 10% scammers following me around. I swiveled around, almost touching noses with the man in a skull cap, and screamed, point blank, "OUT, OUT, OUT," while pointing to the door. "Don't you dare set foot in this shop!" He left but hung around nearby. I had more than my fill with those percentage hustlers. Enough was enough. Finally, I was learning to assert myself and stop those pests from plaguing me so that I could shop in peace.

I spent half an hour sifting through all the merchandise and placed the best pieces on top of the counter, ready to haggle for the lowest price. Waiting for nearly ten minutes, with interspersed yelps, I yelled, "Is any-body home? Hey, I need some help," I finally let out a blood curdling "HELP!"

The 10% man stuck his head around the corner and I shook my finger in his face like an irate school spinster, "What did I say? Out, and I mean NOW! I don't want to see even one toe cross this line." I drew an invisible line with my foot. Another ten minutes and I stepped outside and asked the sticky hustler, "Where the heck is the invisible owner of this shop?" He lowered his head and mumbled, "Mum, I AM the owner of this shop."

Can you imagine? Here I was in macho Muslim-land, bossing around the owner. It was a small victory for women's rights in Kashmir. I followed my system of offering half the asking price. The man nodded, yes.

I then asked for a further discount if I bought everything. He agreed. I left the shop with my bounty, but instead of feeling proud of my bargaining skills, I was positive he got the best of me. I'll never know. I made my other purchases and lugged the stuff back to my hotel room.

I needed a selenite crystal chakra cleaning. Of course, I repented for my erratic behavior; I don't know what had gotten into me. I would do better next time. Actually, I AM a nice person, but I was driven past my tipping point. I'd have to think of a better strategy while shopping and breathe deeply more often 2-3-4. I guess the owner allowed my antics since it was off-season, and he was willing to bend for a sale. I just couldn't afford to get my karma out of whack. (Poor man, perhaps he was henpecked at home and used to ranting women.)

* * *

My round-trip ticket back to Delhi was the following day. I needed to get back to Europe to start earning money, but, after opening up my well-worn Rand McNally world map, I decided to zip over to Egypt and Israel since they were almost on the way back.

My return flight to New Delhi was seamless, and I had become attached to Air India's fleet of World War II prop planes. I spent the night at the Narula Hotel and booked my flight to the land of "Exodus." EgyptAir had a stopover in Jeddah, wherever that was. The agent told me it would be much cheaper if I'd book to my final destination. I didn't want to confuse him by saying, "heaven," so I thought hard and decided on Rome.

He explained the only problem was, there were no flights from Cairo to Tel Aviv. I would have to fly to Cyprus first, then on to Israel. "Why? It's only a hop, skip, and a jump from Egypt to Israel." The agent laughed since he thought I was joking. Oh well, there must have been a good reason, perhaps a strike?

The receptionist retrieved my suitcase from the hotel's musty store-room, and I stuffed my new purchases into my big bag. I was sad that my angel, Arjun, was away and I couldn't give him a hug. I left a note for him and a present from Kashmir. I taxied to the air terminal with my four flight tickets tucked away in my body pouch and dreamed about the adventures awaiting me.

Humming the dramatic theme song from "Exodus," I wondered if Mount Sinai and the Red Sea were very far from Cairo. The AirEgypt aircrafts looked like an upgrade from Air India's fleet. Sneaking into the business class to check-in didn't get me into business class, but it allowed me to get onto the plane quicker, so I could find an overhead with enough space for my bulging tote bag. I wore my comfy, good luck, travel clothes – my embroidered jeans and my yellow tie-dye T-shirt. I just let my hair do what it wanted and left it unrestrained.

* * *

I chose an aisle seat for the five-hour flight to Jeddah, so I didn't have to crawl over someone every time I needed to exercise or 'powder my nose.' There was a middle-aged man of about forty-five fast asleep at the window seat. Great to find someone snoozing, so they wouldn't bother me or ask me my purpose in life. I settled in and began meditating on emptying my mind, which went quickly.

My breathing exercises and mantras were very therapeutic and I felt at peace. However, I wasn't sure if that feeling nurtured me. Perhaps I was addicted to adrenaline. I loved to feel excited and pumped rather than at peace. Peace was boring. I decided to write in my journal.

A mere two hours and lunch was served. I was tempted to tell the hostess my friend didn't want lunch, but I couldn't take the risk of any karma fall-out. My drooling seatmate sat up, wiped his mouth with the back of his hand, adjusted his glasses, and tried to pat his hair into place.

I pretended he didn't exist. I was becoming hardened in my travel etiquette.

He didn't offer an opener, so I continued writing in my journal. The curry and rice lunch arrived with mixed fruit salad and was a great combo, in my opinion. Mr. Seatmate made some complaining noises that I ignored. He then returned to his catatonic deep sleep. Yea! I'd have more time with my own precious thoughts. Looking around, I realized that I was outnumbered, nine to one, by Muslim passengers. Perhaps I should put a scarf over my three feet of frizzy hair to try and fit in with the general `look.'

Ah, let's see what the in-flight magazine suggests I do. I thought I'd get a detailed map of Egypt, but the big article was about Jeddah, described as the gateway to the holy cities of Mecca and Medina. Every Muslim had to make a pilgrimage (*Hajj*) to Mecca at least once in their lifetime. The catch was, they had to go when the Islamic calendar moon-time was right. Well, it looked like the moon was in the correct position according to the number of Islamic devotees on board.

On TV, I'd seen stampedes during these holy gatherings, so I figured it wasn't for me. I'd probably get trampled even if there wasn't a stampede because I defied the dress code or something silly. My fellow passengers didn't look thrilled about their trip of a lifetime. I started to sing the best from "*Hair*" under my breath.

Mr. Drool shifted and awoke, rudely squashing me in an attempt to get to the men's room. "Wait a minute, BUSTER, let me get up." He shot me a look of disdain. We were in a waiting pattern for touchdown to Jeddah. The bumpy landing evoked applause. Those of us going on to Cairo were ordered to remain seated - about five percent, ugh, forty-five minutes before the new passengers poured in. I guess they were the Egyptian Muslims returning from their Holy trip. At least I got a bird's eye view of Saudi Arabia and the Red Sea, which was not red.

After a while, Mr. Seatmate whipped out a well-thumbed glossy magazine titled Archeological Digest. I thought to myself, come on, be nice to the man. "Oh, are you an archeologist?" He retorted cryptically, "Clever young lady, what gives you that idea?" "All the dirt under your fingernails," I heard myself say. "Well, Miss Flower Power has some thorns," he replied with a frightfully British accent. I queried, "Eton? Cambridge? I guess you have enough inheritance to choose such a frivolous métier as archeology?"

I don't know what came over me; not only was I copying his accent, but I took on his sarcastic style. I had engaged in this typical type of verbal touché, table-talk while in London, but how could I imagine it would surface again on a plane from New Delhi to Cairo? How could I know an acid-wit-Brit would be seated next to me on an EgyptAir flight?

"For a hippie colonist from the other side of the pond, you're not bad at throwing your words around," he admitted. I replied in my posh Queen's English, "I suppose you're going to solve the mystery of the architectural feat of the construction of the granite beams of the inner King's Chamber of The Great Pyramid Khufu of Giza?" Mr. know-it-all paled and started to tremble.

"Who are you? Are you a spy?" I responded with confidence, "Well if I am a spy, do you really think I'm going to admit it?" "Who are you? Why did you sit here?" he asked. "I sat here because you were deep sleeping, and I hoped you'd remain that way until we got to Cairo."

"Okay, so what do you know about the King's Chamber of The Great Pyramid of Giza?" he pleaded. "Not much. I only had one semester of archeology at LSU. We studied the three Pyramids of Giza, and the hottest topic was how the King's inner chamber was built of granite and how it held up under the weight of all those tons of stones." I wondered whether it was serendipity or perhaps coincidence that I was seated next to this peculiar archeologist.

He extended his hand and introduced himself; "My name is Dr. Barkley Hastings." "*Bonjour*, I'm Marie France from New Orleans." "Sorry Yankee, I thought you were a dim-wit hippie." "Well, I knew you were an acid-wit-Brit-twit and decided to play your game. And, I'm not a Yankee, I'm a Rebel from south of the Mason-Dixon line." "Okay, okay, you've proven your point."

"I've been studying The Great Pyramid of Giza for nearly ten years now and will be meeting my colleague, a well-known architect, to enter the Pyramid and investigate the granite support beams of the King's inner Chamber. We have a theory."

"If you would like to accompany us, you may. We have permission tomorrow morning from 7 am to 11 am to explore the grand gallery and the King's Chamber. Tours for the general public commence at noon." I tried to look cool, "Let me check my diary. Yes, that fits in perfectly."

Barkley asked me, "By the way, what are you doing in this part of the world?" My answer was sincere, "I'm on a spiritual journey." Barkley admitted, "We have something else in common then; my quest is eternity."

Barkley gave me a card from the Oberoi Hotel and said, "Be sure you're in the lobby by 6 am. It will be cooler at that hour. Do you have anything else to wear?" "Yes, I have some safari type Bermuda shorts and a white T-shirt. How's that for an archeological outfit?" "Perfect, and perhaps you can do something with your hair?" "Yes, Sir." We had time to exchange our experiences in India and waved goodbye, "*Hasta mañana.*"

13. CAIRO

I found my luggage, then skipped to the airport hotel desk to ask for clean, cheap lodgings. The Giza Hotel sounded like the best value for the inner city, not far from the five-star Oberoi. I decided on a quick meal nearby and early in the sack for my pending exploit. I was perplexed by the ten yards long, eight-foot-high walls built on each city block's curb. They looked new but worn, with lots of small chunks of brick missing.

The hotel receptionist explained that they were firewalls. "Are there many fires downtown?" The guy rolled his eyes and said, "No, when there is gunfire, you have a place to run for protection." "Oh, gun-*fire*. Well, I grew up in New Orleans, and it can't be worse than that."

I did make a point of reading *The Herald Tribune* in New Delhi airport, and the Middle-East looked pretty peaceful. It seems Anwar Sadat had made many radical changes in Egypt's direction. He reversed some of the economic and political principles by breaking with the Soviet Union to make Egypt an ally of the US. Initiating the peace process with Israel, he also re-instituted the multi-party system.

But, I guess you can't please everyone all of the time. There will always be opposition. It seemed that 1972 was a good year so far, and in my twelve months of non-stop travels, I'd not seen or heard a single bullet.

Using sound wisdom, I ordered a wake-up call at 5:30 am, which consisted of a loud knock on my door and a man shouting, "WAKE UP!" It worked. I had laid out my beige safari Bermudas and my clean white T-shirt. I wore my hair in a low braid with a single leather strip of turquoise and coral woven in for a bit of oomph. I looked like I was ready for a "dig."

I taxied over to the chic Oberoi Hotel to avoid dodging bullets. I was there punctually at 6 am, and Barkley was waiting in the reception. He introduced me to his colleague, Simon, and we got into a minivan that transported us into another era. It only took us half an hour's drive, including crossing the Nile, to regress 4,500 years - to the days of the ancient Giza Pyramids.

It was a comfort to see Simon wore a neat, low ponytail that artists and architects were prone to sport as a creative statement. Apart from that, he had on khaki-colored trousers and a lightweight linen shirt, well wrinkled. A Nikon camera with mega lens hung from his sturdy neck, and he was carrying a tripod. Simon was relaxed and cheerful, creating an excellent counterbalance to Barkley's intensity.

"WOW!" It was hard to take in the magnitude of the ancient structures. The largest, the Great Pyramid of Giza, is the most ancient of the World's Seven Wonders and best-preserved. The minivan dropped us off about half a mile from the complex, in full desert. Any closer and you couldn't get a full view of the vast dimensions of the Pyramid complex.

The length of each side of the base was nearly eight-hundred feet and the height about five-hundred feet. Simon set up his tripod and took at least thirty shots from different angles.

I had wandered away to look at the approaching camel with his colorful tassels and turbaned driver. Another man with a turban was on foot and they were carrying on a loud conversation. The man on foot hollered, "Camel ride to pyramid." I replied, "No, thank you, walking to the pyramid."

In the same instant, I was hoisted up towards the camel and the driver grabbed my wrist and yanked me upwards. I pulled back and screamed, "No camel!" A tug-a-war was set into motion. I wasn't against a camel ride to the pyramid, but I knew the rip-off price would not fit my budget. Simon ran to my aid and said something in Arabic. The men released me and apologized, "Sorry, Sorry." I asked Simon what the magic words were.

He laughed and said, "My woman, let go." It sounded like cave talk, but it worked.

We walked to the largest structure first, The Great Pyramid Khufu of Giza. The smaller pyramids were built for his two sons, and the broken-down little mounds were built for his wives. That seemed par for the course.

Each of Khufu's stone blocks weighed three to fifteen tons, and there were approximately two million stone blocks. The pyramid took twenty years to build by one hundred thousand oppressed slaves whose average life span was between thirty to thirty-five years. It was mind-boggling and I couldn't handle any more statistics. It was as if Barkley was saying "gib-bel-de-goop-pop-boom." I just couldn't grasp the dimensions but was happy to stand there awe-struck.

The Sphinx, with smaller dimensions, had a lion's body and a man's head. The limestone sculpture is the largest and oldest in Egypt and per-haps the world. It faces the sunrise and guards the pyramid tombs of Giza.

We finally arrived at the north side of the Great Pyramid and climbed about sixty feet upward, from one gigantic stone to the next. Hallelujah, we made it to the massive arched entrance of The Khufu. I felt a *drum roll* in my soul as Barkley gave the guard on duty the secret password for off-hours entry.

The grand gallery was about fifty yards long and twelve yards high, so the gradual incline was a work-out, but do-able. The passage then nar-rowed to three feet five inches high, so we had to struggle up most of the way in a doubled-over position. Near the chamber, there was a step in the floor, and the passage opened up to five feet seven inches.

We stood inside the Pharaoh's final resting place, the burial chamber, slightly hunched, with smiles of satisfaction. King Khufu's stone sarcoph-agus was center stage. His mummy and all the treasure and material goods and offerings had been stolen centuries ago, but a few prized pos-sessions were on show at the Cairo Museum.

From a seated position, I marveled at the architectural feat of the support beams that held this chamber intact for thousands of years. I must admit I prayed that this would not be the day the beams finally gave way. There were some large stress fractures visible.

I sat there in a comfortable lotus position, with my hands resting on my knees, palms upward and my index finger touching my thumb – to demonstrate inner perfection. Also, bringing my thumb and index finger together created a type of circuit, retaining the increased energy I created while meditating. Plus, it was a cool position to be found in if the beams finally gave way.

Sitting there, within the entrails of the pyramid, I couldn't help but catch what Barkley and Simon were discussing in whispers. My hearing was supersonic, which often proved to be a nuisance. Most of their chatter bypassed my attention, but I caught something about their theory that The Great Khufu Pyramid was constructed from the inside out. It was a fascinating idea that wandered through my conscience, momentarily.

I was lost in my own thoughts of pyramidology – the pseudoscientific speculations regarding pyramids, most often the Giza complex. Some pyramidologists claimed that Khufu of Giza had encoded within predictions for Moses' exodus from Egypt, the start of World War I, the founding of modern-day Israel in 1948, and future events of Armageddon.

The triangular shape of the pyramids themselves may have been designed to evoke the rays of the sun streaming between heaven and earth. Once covered with highly reflective white limestone, the Great Khufu emitted a glimmering, polished appearance when viewed from a distance. It was proven that pyramid spaces preserved foods, maintained the sharpness of blades, improved health and were useful as thought-forming chambers.

Also, triangular crystal shapes were key in focusing energy and power. I wasn't sure if I should share all my hypotheses with Barkley and Simon.

Perhaps later, when we were out of their sacred space, they would be more receptive to my illuminating conclusions.

Meanwhile, I used my precious time in the energy chamber to meditate on the meaning of life and eternity. The unusual word "Yeshua" kept weaving itself through my thoughts like a golden thread. I saw a bright light, a light more brilliant than I could ever imagine. Perhaps my higher power, the God of the Universe, was trying to communicate with me. I knew I was in The Throne Room. I was immersed in liquid love.

"Hey, wake up! We have to leave; it's almost noon." I came to my senses with Barkley shaking me and laughing. "I'm not sleeping; I was just in another realm." Simon offered me his hand, "Well, up and out of your trance, Marie France, the descent back to the entrance is rather rigorous." I breathed in love 2-3-4 and expelled negativity 2-3-4. I did a few squats and lunges to stretch the ligaments of my legs.

I couldn't fathom I had been sitting on the floor so long in a lotus position. It seemed like a mere ten minutes. I muttered, "Time flies when you have an encounter." I chalked up the experience of being in that sacred chamber where the King's mummy waited to be transported back to life and into eternity.

We walked about half a mile through the same stretch of desert and found our driver waiting there with the van. "Whew, it's good to get back to some shade. I'd love a swim," I admitted. Barkley picked up on my plea, "If you like, you can use the rooftop pool at the Oberoi whenever you want; just give them my name if they ask."

Little did they know, that was my plan whenever I arrived in a city; I'd had a lovely dip and a swim in the best hotel pools West to East and now back again. It was a question of looking confident. I'd head to the elevator without glancing left or right, then punch the button at the top marked "pool."

It always worked, I brought my bar of soap with me, and I'd have a nice hot shower afterward. Usually, hotel towels were available. If not, I'd shake dry and use the hot air hand blowers to tidy up. My lodging, The Giza, didn't even have tourist brochures or offer tours. There were no other foreigners there. It seemed to be the bleak hotel for Egyptian traveling shoe salesmen, camel traders, or conventions for street vendors.

* * *

As much as I loved my visit to the Giza complex and our private expedition into the King's Chamber, I bowed out for the following days. Barkley and Simon's mission was not mine; I was a culture vulture addicted to museums. Some call it `museum madness,' but whatever it was, I loved to spend hours poring over every artifact. It also helped me identify the real antiques so that I wouldn't fall for an unscrupulous sales pitch.

Of course, I would have loved to have taken a cruise up the Nile, visited the Valley of the Kings in Luxor, explored Cleopatra's hometown of Alexandria and milled around Aswan, but I was running low on travel funds. I would get my act together in Europe and return.

Meanwhile, the King "Tut" (Tutankhamun) collection was on show at the Cairo Museum, plus Nefertiti's bust. She and her husband, Pharaoh Akhenaten, were considered the power couple of their day. The body of King Ramses II, Pharaoh during the time of Moses, was found in the Red Sea and was also on display.

Antony and Cleopatra's long-lost tomb remains a mystery, but Cleopatra was Egypt's last Queen and buried along with the love of her life in thirty BC. At least I'd get to see the coins with her portrait and other bits and bobs during her reign. What a treasure chest full of mummies plus one hundred thousand ancient objects to rummage through - I couldn't wait!

I decided to go on foot to the Egyptian Cairo Museum from my hotel. It was like playing musical chairs. I would run from one firewall to the next, then saunter behind the wall, then run again. I was told to stay near a wall, just in case snipers started up - quite exhilarating.

When I arrived at the edge of Tahrir Square, POW, the imposing, formidable, 1901 Cairo Museum jumped out at me broadcasting its existence in deep pink Rosetta Stone. It was preceded by a grand fountain full of coins, cigarette butts and lily pads. Guarding the collection was a small replica of the nose-less Sphinx, and regal King Palms shot up above the massive museum, like fireworks.

Ta-dum, I felt like Cleopatra entering her palace. I wore my black Moroccan trousers and mirrored crop-top with my upper arm bracelets and a wide headband. I decided on one of my tribal necklaces and heavy eye make-up. I thought it would be appropriate to go for an Egyptian `look,' even if it was a few thousand years late. My hair had become desert-straight due to the arid climate, and I thought about cutting bangs but knew they'd just crinkle up to my hairline with a bit of humidity.

An overhead skylight lit up the main gallery, and the world-class exhibit glistened with the sun's rays. Yikes, too much input was overwhelming – I would design a plan of attack. First, in the main gallery, I turned left and hugged the wall, then looped over to the right wall, finishing up with the middle aisle. The stellar treasures were on the second floor - King Tut's collection, including the golden burial mask and all the mummies!

I was in my element! My main distraction was from the flashing lights. The tourists kept taking photos of me and wanted their kids standing next to me. I put up with individual pictures with each child and then limited to one group photo for each family. Now I knew what Daisy Duck felt like walking around Disneyland. Others thought I was a museum guide and kept asking me questions. I just gave them my default reply, "Upstairs."

I was lost in the magnitude of the museum itself, plus absorbing the thousands of artifacts. This was not a one-off, one-day tour. I had brought a bottle of water with me and snacks, not to lose time by having to go out to eat. I decided to pace myself and do the entire gallery, then zero in on my favorites the next day. When I got upstairs to the mummies, I caught myself singing softly, *"Oh, Mac Pharaoh had a barn, e-i-e-i-o, here a mummy, there a mummy, everywhere a mummy, mummy, e-i-e-i-o...."*

A plump German lady swung around and shushed me with her chubby index finger in front of her puckered lips. I converted my song into a hum, and she turned around and shot me an evil eye. "Have a good day, ma'am," was my smiling reply.

Room fifty-two, jackpot, mummified domestic pets! I was impressed that the Pharaohs wanted their beloved pets along with them in the *after-life*. I was astonished to see that the famed Pharaoh Hound, with its long pointed ears, long legs, and a sleek body was the same as the rabbit hunting hounds in Ibiza – officially called the Ibizan Hound. Such a noble breed.

It was already 6 pm, and a warning bell advised visitors to head to the exit immediately. I couldn't wait to return for another full day. I skipped back to my hotel, faster between the bullet-marred protective walls. The receptionist handed me a note along with my key. "We hope you can join us for supper at seven in the Moghul Room at the Oberoi. Barkley."

* * *

Perfect timing, I'd change clothes to something more archeological and pop my bikini, a bar of soap and toothbrush into my bag. Ah yes, my thin cashmere shawl would add a touch of class to my sandy pyramid ensemble and combat the chilly night's drop to 50º F. I grabbed a taxi since they were cheap and dusk was falling.

The stately hotel doorman opened the taxi door and ushered me into the lobby as if I were royalty. The shawl did wonders and perhaps it was my well-styled straighter hair that I dramatically swooshed over to one side, leaving my left ear exposed with five tiny golden hoops and a dangling earring. I had come to realize by now that my wild, frizzy hair gave the wrong message. It seemed to broadcast, "Beware, I am a hippie, druggie, shoplifter." At least that was the vibe I got.

Both Barkley and Simon were in the lobby to greet me - Simon whistled softly with approval. After all, I had to remember the prophecy my friend Rise sent me off with when I left for Paris. I had to visualize myself modeling in Paris and beyond. I reflected on Dale Carnegie's Course, "How to Win Friends and Influence People." Carnegie had tapped into people's desire to have more self-confidence. He said, "Confidence begets confidence."

Barkley nodded to me with approval and said, "That's more like it, young lady. What a make-over from the hippie-Hannah I woke up next to on the plane. No, you can't tell a book by its cover. Who would have thought you were actually a nice, clever, level-headed, attractive, witty lady?" I admitted, "You're not the first person to say so," and laughed.

As we entered the chic Mughal Restaurant, I felt as if I were back in Kashmir. I wasn't impressed with Egyptian food, especially the reheated junk I had eaten in the cheap-o places near my hotel. Barkley recommended giant champagne and lemon prawn as a starter, then as the main dish, *rogan josh*, an aromatic lamb dish, and one of Kashmiri cuisine's signature recipes. I smiled and said with confidence, "Superb, my favorite." I hadn't a clue what the main course was, but I liked everything eatable and was always hungry.

"So, what have you guys been up to? What is your latest pyramid revelation?" I found the British a bit reticent to speak about topics more personal than 'the weather.' I guess they found Americans a bit too forward and intrusive. Barkley was caught by surprise and cleared his throat while Simon glanced down. I read their body language; they had discovered something big and tonight was a celebration.

I answered my question for them, "Well, I knew you would unearth a new theory, my intuition, I guess." Barkley and Simon locked eyes for a second, then Barkley said, "Actually we did; it was while you were on the floor in a trance."

"Well, I knew something was happening in the King's Chamber since I received an amazing download while I was there." They made eye contact again. I think they thought I might have had something to do with their revelation. "Exactly what kind of download did you receive?" I told them, "I was taken into another realm and given a `YES' word, and then I was saturated in liquid-love and I saw a light, white as snow, then other lights like a blazing fire."

Simon asked me, "What kind of `Yes' word?" "YESHUA," floated from my lips. Barkley gulped. I thought I would give them a kick and added, "It seems The Great Khufu Pyramid was built from the inside out." Barkley coughed, and part of his champagne and lemon prawn shot out of his mouth and bounced off the table. My last comment had obviously shaken Barkley. I kept my blasé attitude but chuckled inwardly. I think they must have thought I was a soothsayer of sorts.

I didn't want to ruin their meal, so I started to talk about the weather. They needed to get back onto safe ground. I began to feel guilty about pretending to have had an intuitive revelation about the Pyramid being built inside out. At the end of the meal, I confessed that my hearing is over-sensitive, and I heard them speaking about it. Barkley and Simon locked their gaze once again and Barkley admitted they had said absolutely nothing about that theory, but it occurred to both of them while I was in a trance. They had only spoken about it later in their hotel.

Now I started to feel a bit uneasy. I wondered exactly what had happened while we were in the entrails of that massive stone structure. One thing was clear; I could revert back to the sensation of liquid love and tap into that exquisite experience at will. It could only have come from the God of love, the Creator of the universe communicating with me. But why then and there, and why did it involve these two archeologists? They didn't look like seekers or very spiritual; however, Barkley did say that he was searching for eternity. Oh well, I'd think about it later. After all, tomorrow is another day.

We exchanged business cards, and Barkley made me promise when I was next in London, I'd look him up. Simon lived in Cambridge but said he'd come down to London for the day, so we could have lunch together and reminisce about our enlightened morning in the mystical belly of the pyramid. I had one more day to hang out in the museum, and then the following morning, I was off to Israel via Cyprus. We exchanged fraternal hugs, and my newly-made friends offered to see me to my hotel. "Thanks, guys, but I thought I might swim first if you don't mind." "No, you'll have the pool to yourself at this hour.....enjoy your splash." I waved goodbye and ducked into the elevator, and zoomed up to the penthouse pool. I needed a cool dip, then a hot shower, and a clean hand basin to polish up my white, slight overbite.

I decided to tone down my apparel for my last day at the Cairo Museum. That way, I'd have more peace, thus more time to study the trillion artifacts awaiting me. I guess the choice of my decent, beige safari shorts and plain white T-shirt made people think I was a guide, so once again, I was bombarded with questions - but at least I was spared the flashing cameras. It was relaxing to feel anonymous for short periods. But, to tell you the truth, I am an attention seeker.

Perhaps this malady was triggered by the attentiveness lavished on my brother when we were growing up – I had to fight for recognition. I attributed it to his big blue eyes and blond, straight hair, perfect teeth, and even features. He was born with muscles and excelled at everything; plus, he was helpful to our parents.

In my search for affirmation, I discovered I could sing. By the time I was eight, I had memorized eighteen songs. I listened to my folks' big, breakable 78 RPM records over and over again to build up my repertoire. When visitors came to our home, my mom would generously offer, "Honey, would you like to sing us a song?" The tune that drew me the most accolades was "Let me go Lover," by the duo Jenny Lou Carson and Al Hill.

As I grew from a petite girl into a beanstalk at age twelve, I discovered that I had a shot at becoming popular by becoming the class clown. I was usually voted president of my class and was even elected Home Coming Queen. I got to ride around the football field on a Cadillac convertible, sitting above the back seat, on the rim of the trunk. However, while wearing the red cape, crown and waving my wand, I felt like an imposter. I pulled off that stunt because there were always more girls in my classes than boys, and what girl wants to vote for a beautiful, overachieving peer? I rest my case.

14. CYPRUS

As usual, I wore my lucky travel outfit since it had always secured my good fortune. My embroidered jeans embodied memories from each exciting leg of my journey, and my yellow tie-dye T-shirt was happy and sunny and not too dirty. I wore my hair in a ponytail pulled back from my face, so my left ear and five earrings would be visible – creating an interesting focal point. The flight was only an hour and forty-five minutes from Cairo to the Larnaca International Airport of Cyprus. I planned on only one night in Nicosia. The airport's local bus was cheap, and the terminal was located in the heart of the capital city.

The last window seat of the prop plane was on the 3rd row next to a stodgy looking businessman. It seems his wife preferred an aisle seat too; therefore, they screamed across the aisle vehemently. It sounded like they were Greek, rather than Turkish Cypriots, meaning they were probably Orthodox Christians. I wondered if they wanted to convert a wayward-looking hippie. I seemed to broadcast that I needed to be saved. Thus far, airplanes, trains, and buses were the major assigned places (by my higher power) for me to receive enlightenment on a variety of spiritualities.

I figured that my plane-mate didn't speak English, so I retrieved my battered journal from my tote bag and started to scribble down the rest of the amazing things that occurred while I was in Egypt and mainly when I was inside the pyramid.

After about an hour and a half of peace, my seat-partner introduced himself as Mr. Constantinou and pointed across the aisle and said, "My wife." Mrs. said, "Hello, young lady, where are you from?" I wanted to say, "I am an extraterrestrial from the land of Kryptonite," but I was afraid she'd believe me. "Hello, I am Marie France from America."

It was as if they'd made a bet from which country I hailed, and they wanted to know who won. Mrs. Constantinou said proudly, "I told you so." Mr. C then asked, "And what brings you to our fair country?" I admitted, "I'm going to Israel, but was obliged to fly via Cyprus for political reasons." Mrs. C smiled at her husband and said, "I told you so." "Do you know anyone in Cyprus?" he queried. I wondered if this was a loaded question and where this conversation was going. Did they want to adopt me or perhaps offer me money to smuggle something or even sell me into the slave trade?

You heard so much weird stuff about people who fit their description. "They seemed like such a normal, well to do, nice couple. Who on earth would have ever guessed they had three hippies locked up in their basement for the past five years." I was usually not paranoid, but they had an eerie vibe.

Mr. C went on to explain to me that he dealt in precious and semi-precious gems. I thought, man, you're barking up the wrong tree. "You are wearing a stunning, emerald-cut diamond," he added. Wow, I had forgotten that I was wearing the diamond ring my Aunt Charlotte had given me. It was like an extension of my index finger - I hadn't taken it off for at least three years. No one had mentioned it to me before; I guess they thought it was crystal or glass. I replied, "Thanks, my aunt gave it to me."

"Perhaps you would like to join us for dinner at the Hilton Hotel. Belly-dancing starts at 9 pm, and we could meet to eat at 7:30 pm. And, perhaps, I could show you some special gems." Maybe American hippies had bought gems from him in the past. At least I now clocked the motive of this overly-friendly, middle-aged couple. He also commented on my Rolex Oyster wristwatch. "Yes, it's very faithful – I never have to take it off. It's been dipped into many oceans and seas, and it's still ticking."

146

"I imagine you have Israeli relatives you are going to visit?" I just smiled without answering him. I was relieved that he thought I was a rich hippie Jewess who might buy a cut-priced gem from him.

Why not? "Yes, thanks, I'll be there at 7:30 this evening." I joined the couple at the Hilton Inn's fine-dining Olympian Restaurant, wearing a sober outfit with my shawl slung over one shoulder. Mrs. whispered something to hubby, and they smiled and greeted me as if I was a gift from Aphrodite, the ancient goddess of love and beauty and the divine patroness of their fair island. "We reserved the best seats for viewing the show afterward." "Oh, how very thoughtful of you both - I have never seen a 'live' belly-dance show before. This will be a real treat."

I'd decided to order something cheap, so I wouldn't feel too guilty about leading this husband and wife sales-team on a wild goose chase. "They have the best *souvlakis* (grilled meat kabobs), plus *afella* (pork marinated in coriander) as well as fried *halloumi* cheese. Olives, pitta bread, and *kolokasi* (root vegetables) are included with the main courses."

Trying to be polite, I said I would eat just a little bit to try Cyprian specialties. They insisted on ordering all the dishes they mentioned and agreed I needed to get some meat on my bones. I was salivating at the thought and cooed, "Well, if you insist, I'll do my best." They were stunned at the quantity of food I woofed down, without taking time to breathe or speak. When my blood sugar was at a low ebb, it was embarrassing how much I devoured.

The Master of Ceremonies announced very proudly, "And here we have the famous dancers; the best belly-dancers in Cyprus – Ira and Ulker." There was a whopping round of applause. Ira was about 5'10" and built like an Olympic shot-put champion. Ulker, on the other hand, was very short and square. Her bare midriff displayed absolutely no signs of a waistline. They both had ample bellies and matching outfits.

Of course, I thought these ladies were the warm-up comedy skit that preceded the real dancers. I didn't know if I should laugh or applaud.

I looked to my hosts and followed their lead – they were applauding with enthusiasm. The music started up, and the dancers took off like poetry in motion. They started with swan-like movements, working their way to the expressively erotic, but in such a graceful way. I realized that rhythmic bumps and grinds had nothing to do with body shape. It seems that their large pot-bellies propelled the centrifugal force needed to keep their gyrating flesh in motion. I sat there, motionless in awe.

They received a standing ovation – I found myself on my feet cheering and whistling like a truck driver. A piano player continued plinking out background music, and after about twenty minutes, Mr. C took four small, red velvet bags from his pocket. Most of the diners had gone, and the tables around us were empty. He opened the first bag and dumped out the contents onto the tablecloth—three blue stones of different sizes.

"These are the best sapphires you'll ever have the opportunity to touch," bragged Mr. C. I picked one up, breathed on it, and studied whether or not the fog disappeared quickly. It was real; the vapor evaporated immediately. He handed me an eye loop, and I studied it for impurities; it was flawless. "A real beauty," I replied. I really didn't want to waste the man's time and get his hopes up, so I decided to end his misery quickly. I whispered, "To tell you the truth, I'm looking for Tanzanite, Black Opal and Alexandrite."

Those three gems are the rarest and most expensive in the world. I was gambling on the odds that his other three bags were void of those rare gems. His face dropped, and he admitted, "Apart from these sapphires, I only have diamonds, rubies and emeralds." Poor guy, I cheered him up by asking for his business card and gave him mine. I reminded him to stay in touch. I added, "It's safe to send gems by registered mail since it includes up to $500,000 insurance." He must have thought I was the great-granddaughter of Baron Rothschild and heir to his banking fortune. I was glad I had taken that free gem course, offered by Adler's Jewelers on Canal St., back in New Orleans.

I thanked the Constantinous for the scrumptious meal and the spectacular show. I was glad they had gotten out and had some fun. And indeed, it was a break from their hum-drum existence. I excused myself and reminded them that I had an early flight the next morning, and I wished them well.

We parted in the Hilton lobby; I waved goodbye and entered the elevator. Bingo! Just as I thought, the pool was on the top floor. I was glad I remembered to pop a bar of soap, a bikini, and a toothbrush into my bag.

Returning to my crummy hotel feeling squeaky clean, I looked forward to a new adventure - ISRAEL. I conjured up memories of Joseph and Mary trudging their way to Bethlehem, where the inns were filled, so they had to sleep in a stable. And there in a manger, baby Jesus was born. I wondered how much of that Christmas story was real and how much was a myth. Too bad it coincided with the arrival date of Santa Claus, who quickly eclipsed the stable event. I attended Sunday school until I was twelve, then I went to real church with my friend Beth, since her dad was the preacher... ...until they left town when I was fourteen.

Having acquired new respect, I had a bolstered interest and a healthy curiosity about the Prophet Jesus. It seemed that the other spiritualities I had encountered revered Jesus and accepted him as an outstanding philosopher and teacher. I hoped to discover more about his teachings and his perspective. I wanted to know what had captured the interest of Mahatma Gandhi, that he was ready to turn his back on Hinduism and embrace Jesus and Christianity.

15. ISRAEL

Cyprus Airways, being the cheapest choice, was on par with Air India. It was only an hour and a half to the Ben Gurion Airport in Tel Aviv, and luckily I had a backpacker next to me who slept the entire trip. I wore my lucky jeans and tie-dye T-shirt and was feeling optimistic about my upcoming revelations.

When I retrieved my suitcase from baggage pick-up, I merrily skipped to the bus terminal for the hour and a half ride to the famed city of Jerusalem. I couldn't wait to discover more about the prophet Jesus and walk where he had walked.

The bus stopped directly in front of "Tourist Information." How convenient is that? It must be because of my lucky outfit. It was starting to drizzle, so I ducked into the modern info center. There was a lady with bright orange hair and a smug expression. I told her I wanted an inexpensive hotel and without looking up, I thought I heard her say, "Go away."

"What?" I couldn't believe what I heard. She then said, "Abraham Hostel." Scribbling down the address, which was illegible, she then shoved it to me without lifting her gaze. By now, it was raining cats and dogs, so I said meekly, "Will you please call a taxi?" She made a "humph" noise and called a taxi, then said – "Wait outside."

"Excuse me," I replied. "Have you noticed there is a raging storm out there?" She glanced out the window and replied, "You cannot wait here." I thought, maybe I'm on Candid Camera. This *is* Tourist Information? I am the only person in this office, and this snotty employee is telling me to wait outside in the rain. I wanted to demand the manager, but she was clearly the boss and was certainly not trying to promote tourism in Jerusalem.

I realized that aggressiveness was a manifestation of pain. I refused to receive her offensive behavior personally. Perhaps she had marital problems or an ingrown toenail. I prayed for her while waiting to check into the Abraham Hostel. A carbon copy of the tourist info lady, also with red hair, was rude to the point of abusive. She pushed me the key without looking up and said, "No men allowed in your room."

It was apparent these Jewish ladies flunked their course on "people-skills." I had just experienced a year of kind people bending over backward to please me. Perhaps only to coax some money out of my pocket, but it felt good. I was not prepared for this unexpected bucket of cold water to be dumped on me so abruptly.

Everywhere I went, shop people had the same impolite attitude. It finally dawned on me that the Jews here in Israel were in survival mode. The Jewish nation was without a homeland for thousands of years. They had been driven out of most nations in Europe and globally ostracized, not to mention the Holocaust and the Inquisition. Here they were, a tiny country surrounded by powerful Muslim nations, like sitting ducks. What drew them from their safe, affluent lifestyles abroad? It was as if they were "homing-pigeons" programmed to return to their ancient homeland.

The Jewish people had to be tough; without being thick-skinned and resilient, they'd have been swallowed up centuries ago. After all, the most brilliant scientists, doctors, lawyers, composers, philosophers, physicists, bankers, jewelers, producers, directors, actors and comedians in the US are Jewish. But they only make up 2.2% of the population. That is the perfect formula for envy. Jewish independence had been lost in Israel 2,000 years ago and restored only twenty-five years ago. I decided they had a free ticket to be rude.

After all, they took one look at me and decided I would not improve their economy or anything else. I understood that they tagged me as an immoral hippie, and that was that. I would get on with my plan of enjoying the Land of Jesus, even if his people rejected me also.

* * *

My first stop was the Western Wall, better known as the Wailing Wall. I was pleased that my hostile hostel was situated in Old Jerusalem. That ancient city offered a maze of narrow alleyways and historical architecture that characterized its four quarters: Jewish, Muslim, Christian and Armenian. Old Jerusalem is surrounded by a fortress-like stone wall and home to some of the world's holiest sites.

It was surprising to see so many Orthodox Jews praying and swaying there and placing prayer requests in the cracks of the Wailing Wall. It most certainly was not just a tourist attraction. It was a place of prayer and pilgrimages sacred to the Jewish people. It is believed that Divine Presence rests upon the Wall, and all prayers soar to Heaven through the adjoining Temple Mount.

The Wall is the only remains of the second temple of Jerusalem, held to be uniquely holy by the ancient Jews and destroyed by the Romans in 70AD. I decided to write out a prayer to stick in a crack. "Dear God, I am listening. Please speak to me." Then I rocked back and forth from the waist, Orthodox style, to give it a good send-off.

It was fascinating to observe the Orthodox custom when Bar Mitzvah boys and men sported long Shirley Temple side-lock curls and elegant black fedoras. The wide-brimmed black hats, made in Italy, retained the Italian name, Borsalino. I was an accessory-freak, and hats were at the top of my list. They gave the wearer a provocative flair, but at the tune of $350 per hat, I'd look for a copy. It seems the Hasidic Jews wore the black hats to remind themselves constantly that God is above them in heaven.

I noticed that most Jews covered their heads when praying, attending the synagogue, or at a religious event. The non-Orthodox men wore the *Kippah* skullcap. I wondered if balding men stuck their caps on with bubble gum. The women wore scarves. These head coverings show devotion, respect and fear of God. I would look for some skullcaps in the bazaar since they're easy to pack.

Nearby was the Temple Mount – Dome of the Rock Mosque. The Jews acknowledge that the rock on which the Dome was built to be the Holy of Holies. It's where God's divine presence is manifested, and the direction Jews turn towards during prayer. On the other hand, Muslims consider the Dome of the Rock Mosque to be the third holiest shrine in the Muslim world - it is said to be the place from which Muhammad ascended into Allah's presence.

Christians claim that the Temple Mount's worn steps are the very stones that Jesus climbed as he entered and exited the temple when he was but a child. I ran up and down the steps several times for good measure.

Since my hostel insinuated that I was a "floozy," I decided to wear my clean jeans and a nun-type blouse with long sleeves. I pulled back my hair severely in a low ponytail. I wondered if I should wear a cross, a skullcap and a veil, not to offend anyone. After all, as a double-Libra, I was always doing a balancing act. One needs to be tolerant and all-encompassing – different strokes for different folks.

After milling around the courtyards in front of the Dome, I decided to visit the Christian quarter and especially the sacred Church of the Holy Sepulcher. This famous church, initially built in 335AD by the first Christian Roman Emperor, Constantine, is central to the story of Jesus – his death, crucifixion and resurrection. This Byzantine masterpiece was conquered, destroyed, and rebuilt, with every layer of its earth revealing a different piece of the past.

What good fortune! Gathered in front of the church was a small group led by an American guide who looked like a football defense-star in his prime. I merged into the holy huddle and listened with interest. It seems the Crusaders had rebuilt the present massive entrance in the 12th century.

We moved forward as a single unit into the entrance of the church. I caught a glimpse of the name tag of our guide, Jonathan Kramer. He spoke with the zeal of a Baptist televangelist but sported a Jewish name. He wasn't your run-of-the-mill guide; he spoke from the heart, but with authority. He led the way up some steep stone steps, so worn they dipped in the middle. There was a hush of reverence when we arrived at the next floor.

Pointing, Jonathan said, "The stone mound to the right is the place Jesus was crucified, Golgotha, better known as Calvary." I remembered singing long ago at church, something about Jesus going to Calvary and there he died for me. It never really made sense, but now it was taking on some significance. But I wondered if he really died for ME.

The Golgotha stone was behind a barrier. But, there was a spot you could squat down under a low, stone-type altar and stick your hand into a dark hole and touch the sacred rock. I got in line and was grateful to have such an informative guide. I would have never figured out what all the stuff represented in this antique church without his explanation.

When I touched the stone, it sent goose-bumps all over my body, and then I heard an audible voice clearly saying YESHUA. That's all I remembered; when I opened my eyes, I saw Jonathan peering intently at me. "Are you okay?" I wasn't sure - what was I doing sprawled out on that cold, stone floor? "Ah, I guess I'm alright; what happened?" "It seems you forgot about the stone altar above you and bashed your head against it while getting up."

My first thought was, help, now I've been found out. After sneaking so subtly into the tour group, I had become the center of attention. I was never good at doing things discreetly. Jonathan offered me his hand, "Try and get up slowly - at least you're not bleeding." I was somewhat disappointed; I thought it might be appropriate if I shed some blood at Calvary, along with Jesus. There was a bump forming on the top of my head, but luckily my thick wavy hair cushioned the blow.

Jonathan asked me to close my eyes, extend my arm, and slowly bring my hand towards my face, touching my nose with my index finger.

"Perfect," he announced. "You don't have a concussion. What is your name, where are you from, how old are you...." I passed the 'sound-mind' exam. "By the way, how did you connect with this group from the Calvary Chapel Church of Jefferson City, Missouri?" I was rarely at a loss for words, "Ah, at the front door of this church, I'm from a sister-church in Louisiana." I would feign amnesia if questioned by members of that church.

I felt intuitive that something earth-shattering had happened when I touched that sacred stone, but for the life of me, I couldn't remember. Perhaps it would surface later. Back down the steep steps we went, then over to the tomb of Jesus. It looked like a stone chapel within the church. There was an open Byzantine dome strategically placed over the chapel of the tomb of Jesus. Egyptian Orthodox Christians were chanting in the background and swinging ornate silver balls. It looked surrealistic, with the smoke from their incense drifting through the beam of light glowing from the open dome surrounding the tomb.

We entered the chapel in smaller groups, and I was shocked to see all the religious paraphernalia of golden objects, candelabras and embroidered crosses on red velvet. It defied the simplicity of a cave-like tomb. Over to one side was a simple, single slab of stone, where the body of Jesus was said to be laid.

I was the last to leave; I needed time alone to visualize the empty tomb without all the Orthodox and Catholic décor. I could identify with Mary Magdalene, who went to look in the tomb for Jesus. I could imagine an earthquake and an angel of the Lord coming down from heaven, rolling back the stone in front of the tomb and sitting on it. At that split second, I felt a tremor, and there was a blinding flash of white light. It was a déjà vu of my pyramid experience. My vision was interrupted when I heard a voice calling, "Marie France, we're leaving."

Jonathan explained that the original chapel built over Christ's tomb was damaged and three successive chapels had been built over it, like

Russian dolls, one encapsulating the other. However, stripped-down, the original chapel encased the empty tomb in a grotto.

Others insisted that the crucifixion, burial and resurrection of Jesus took place outside the walls of Jerusalem. However, initially, this burial site WAS outside the walls of Jerusalem. The present walls around the city were rebuilt in the 16th century as Jerusalem expanded.

* * *

Jonathan announced, "Now we're off to Cenacle, the ʿUpper Room' over King David's tomb and a Jewish Synagogue. I call it The Apostles Church. Afterward, we'll have a lunch break; then we'll bus to Bethlehem to visit the birthplace of Jesus." I reflected on my good fortune: what a golden opportunity - kind people, informative guide, and free transportation.

While we toured the "Apostles Church," I was fascinated by how Jonathan described the Last Supper. He insisted, "They ate in a horseshoe formation, reclining on the floor, contrary to the famous painting by Leonardo da Vinci." He interspersed his talk with Bible verses he knew by heart, and he spoke about Jesus as if he was a friend - as if Jesus was alive and conversing with him. I admired his passion for what he believed to be true.

Jonathan spoke with passion about the Apostles' waiting in the Upper Room for the Holy Spirit, which would empower them to carry the message of eternal life to the ends of the earth. He said there was a sound like a violent wind, then tongues of fire appeared on the Apostles and disciples' heads, signifying the Holy Spirit. Then they spoke in foreign languages.

How amazing, I thought, even more colorful than rituals in Hindu Ashrams and Buddhist Temples. I had never heard about the Holy Spirit in my brief church experience. Perhaps he was barred from Louisiana because each state in the US is given the right to vote in its own laws and is self-governed.

We passed through the Synagogue on the way to King David's tomb, and I only saw young men. One group holding hands, dancing in a circle and others were rocking out with their typical front to back sway. Some twirled their side-locks - nothing as dull as the churches I had experienced back home.

* * *

Jon (my nickname for Jonathan) announced, "Lunch break! We will all meet back in front of the Wailing Wall to go to Bethlehem at 3 pm." The historical manger was only about seven miles from Old City Jerusalem. The stories that were read to me repeatedly from my illustrated Bible as a kid started to take form and come to life. I'd have some street food at the kabob shop we passed and still have time to jot down my impressions from this morning's events before meeting at the Wall.

As we took our places on the bus, I was aware that I was the youngest sightseer on Jon's tour. The group, mostly over fifty, was dozing off one by one. I decided to get into the mood by singing "Silent Night." Within minutes, the oldies were roused and joined me. We were only on our fourth round by the time the bus pulled up to our destination. I was slightly disappointed that the stable didn't fit the picture in my Bible. I imagined a real barn with some donkeys, straw on the floor, the empty crib.

Helena, the mother of King Constantine, had asked her son to construct "The Church of the Nativity" in 325AD to encompass and commemorate Jesus' birthplace. We had to duck to enter the main entrance of the colossal church. The door's top beam was lowered in the 11th century to prevent Crusaders from galloping in on their horses. The length of the church was the same as a football field.

Jon explained that he was an archeologist, completing his postgraduate studies in Israel. He had spent almost two years excavating parts of this very church we were exploring. Many artifacts were found from the time of Jesus, and even deeper digs revealed objects from King David's reign in one thousand BC. Secular historians, during the time of Jesus, also agreed that this site was accurate. Bull's eye!

Houses were usually built over stone caves in those days, supplying a natural foundation and a place for their livestock to live. Therefore the stable WAS a cave with animals, and the infant Jesus was laid in the feeding trough `manger,' post-partum.

Navigating the low entrance by doubling over, I then zoomed into the church to find the birthplace of Jesus before several other groups beat me to it. I tended to be proactive while touring and did my own thing but stayed close enough to nip back for the narration. We had to walk down ten slippery marble steps to arrive at the basement cave birthplace marked by a huge brass fourteen-pointed star. I felt like doing a Comanche rain dance around the multi-pointed star. I was so pumped but chose to exert self-control and took a deep breath 2-3-4.

Jon gave a long spiel about the probability that this was the exact spot. I clapped and started a wave of jubilant applause that echoed throughout the cave. He knew his stuff, off the cuff—no notes or cheat-sheets.

After wandering around the enormous church and courtyard for almost an hour, we were given the signal to head back to the bus. I was chatting away with a certain Mrs. Philpot when I miscalculated the exit height and clipped my head. I saw stars. I thought that was just a comic book expression, but I really saw thousands of stars. At the same moment, my memory was jolted, and I recalled the audible word I'd heard at Golgotha... ...YESHUA. It was the same Egyptian word that intruded my thoughts when I was inside the pyramid in some sort of trance.

* * *

When the bus deposited us back to Old Jerusalem, Jon invited me for a coffee, and I grabbed the opportunity to quiz him on my knock-out word and ask him how a nice Jewish boy knows so much of the "forbidden" New Testament.

There was a quaint café, not far from the Wall, that Jon said had the best coffee. I was still rattled by the day's events. I told Jon that he was the best guide I'd ever had the privilege to listen to, and I had absorbed a wealth of information in a few short hours. He smiled and said, "Yes, it's my passion, as well as a side-job. I was relieved I didn't have to cut the tour short to rush you to a hospital." "Ha! I am very hard-headed," I admitted.

I explained to Jon, "I casually wrote a prayer request to my higher power and tucked it into the Western Wall this morning. Shortly afterward, I joined your tour. Then when I stuck my hand into the hole to touch the rock that Jesus was crucified on, I heard an audible voice, and then I blanked out. After that, when I was alone in the chapel with the tomb of Jesus, I felt a tremor and saw flashing, blinding white lights. The vision seemed to evaporate when I heard you shout, "We're leaving." Finally, I whacked my head on the low beam of the church exit on our way out. The impact jolted my memory, and I remembered what the audible voice said when I touched the Golgotha stone."

"Wow, girl, you sure seem to be accident-prone." Jon looked at me seriously and asked, "I don't mean to be too personal, and I'm not judgmental, but do you take drugs?" I laughed and admitted, "No, I'm just spaced-out and a bit of a klutz." "Do you mind telling me what the audible word was that you heard?" I admitted that the same word was planted in my mind when I was inside The Giza Pyramid near Cairo. I confessed, "It sounds like an Arabic word.....*YESHUA*." Jon's eyes widened, "Are you sure that's what you heard audibly at Golgotha?" "Absolutely sure – I was so surprised it was the same word I received in the King's Chamber within the pyramid that I forgot about the stone altar above my head and banged into it." Jon remained silent for a few minutes, and I was afraid he thought I was off-my-rocker.

I volunteered, "You see, the prayer I scribbled and stuck into a crack of the Wall this morning said, `Dear God, I am listening, please speak to me.' Do you think there's a connection?" Jon remained silent and nodded his head. After another few minutes of silence, he asked me if I knew Jesus. I said, "Sort of." "What do you mean sort of?" "Well, I learned about him in Sunday school as a kid."

"But this past year, I have been on a spiritual journey through Thailand, Malaysia, Bali, Nepal, India, Kashmir, Egypt and now, here in Israel. I am searching for the Truth and have found bits and pieces along the way – including the importance of Jesus as a top prophet, philosopher and teacher." More silence. I then confessed, "I gate-crashed your tour and am not a member of the Calvary Chapel Church in Louisiana." Jon had a hearty laugh, "That was obvious, but we all thought you would benefit from the tour. You became our mission project." Then I had a deep belly laugh, "Oh, how embarrassing." Jon added, "Yeah, you looked like someone who would liven up the tour, and you did!"

"Well, do you have a Muslim friend who might be able to translate the word Yeshua?" Jon said, "No need, I can translate it." "Well, I hope it's not something awful." "No, it is not; on the contrary, it's something awesome. YESHUA is Hebrew for Joshua." I was confused, "Who's Joshua?" Jon explained that the name JESUS is derived from Yeshua and Joshua. It is based on the Semitic meaning `to deliver, to rescue.'"

"Wow! I wonder why I didn't get the word JESUS." "I guess It's because Jesus was giving you his proper name - Y'shua, but phonetically pronounced Yeshua." "Do you think Jesus was speaking to insignificant me? Don't you think he knows I'm American - he should have just used his American name." Jon added, "Well, it says in the Bible, those who seek shall find." Jon's expression sobered, "I think God has a special mission for you." I found Jon's synopsis too challenging - I wasn't ready for a special mission. I had too many things to do and too many places to discover. I would think about it another day. I changed the subject.

* * *

"Hey Jon, tell me your story. How did a guy with a Jewish name end up becoming an authority on Jesus?" Jon shrugged, "It's a long story." "Well, give me the short version," I pleaded. "First of all, let me guess. You were a great football player, and your parents said you had to give up football and become a doctor like your brother." Jon laughed, "You're very intuitive." I replied, "Yep, that's what they tell me, but it's obvious you played football seriously, probably left tackle. Your neck muscles reveal you did a lot of heavy-duty blocking, and the highest-paid defensive position in the NFL (National Football League) is left tackle."

"Well, Marie France, I'm impressed with your observations," Jon admitted. I explained, "I spent two semesters living in the Tulane, Newcomb dormitory, surrounded by Jewish princesses. They were incorruptible. I had my own car and tried to entice them to join me for a breeze around the French Quarter clubs or a game of bridge. No go, my roommate, Leah Goldstein, told me that if she didn't get 100% on her exams, not even 99%, her parents would disown her, not just punish her. At least she had a motivation to study; I didn't."

"Okay, Jon, what is your story?" He finally cleared up the mystery, "I was awarded a football scholarship to CU (Columbia University) with a clear understanding that I would not turn professional. My mother insisted that Jewish boys do not become professional athletes. They become doctors, lawyers, or bankers. So I compromised and majored in natural sciences, social sciences and humanities. They were disappointed but figured it was better than professional football." "Do they know you believe in Jesus?" "Yes, that's why they agreed to allow me to come to Jerusalem to do my post-graduate studies in archeology. They figured the local Rabbi Ovadia, a personal friend of the family, would straighten me out."

"Well, I hope they don't discover you're leading Christian tours." "But they're not 'Christian tours,' they're tours about the Holy Places in Jerusalem. You see, I don't consider myself a Christian. I value my Jewish heritage. I am a Messianic Jew." "Oh yeah?" I questioned, "And what exactly is that?" "It's a Jew who believes Jesus is THE Messiah – the anointed one who delivered humanity from its sins. The Jews believe that the Messiah has not yet come. But it is so clear in our Torah. All prophecies fulfilled by Jesus in the New Testament are prophesied in our very own Torah, often a millennium in advance. The place Jesus would be born, the details of his death, burial and resurrection. They are events that Jesus could never have manipulated. The Jewish people have been blinded."

"But how did you first discover that Jesus was the Messiah?" I asked. Jon admitted, "He revealed himself to me. It was a lightning bolt encounter, similar to your experiences." "Oh," was all I could muster. "So how much longer will you stay in Israel?" Jon smiled and said, "I guess until Rabbi Ovadia convinces me I am mistaken. I love it here in Israel. This is my homeland, even if I accept Jesus as the Messiah. You know, Jesus was Jewish, and he still is. He is alive and reigning. There are quite a few other Messianic Jews here, so I have lots of company." He seemed a bit fanatical but to each his own.

We exchanged visiting cards, and I thanked Jon again for allowing me to join his tour and not blowing my cover. He smiled a wholesome, happy smile and handed me a small book. It was a tiny Bible with the New Testament plus the Psalms. I guess he was disappointed that he couldn't check me off his list, "converted." "God bless you, Marie France, keep searching and remember it's not about rules or regulations, it's about a relationship with the King. It's not about your good works; it's about His grace."

I honestly felt bad for Jon – I knew he was disheartened that I wasn't as enthusiastic about Jesus as he was. I was impressed that my Higher Power was connecting with me in such powerful ways. I remembered the infusion of love I felt in the Pyramid and knew I was on the right track. My God was all-inclusive and tolerant; he loved everyone. Only *one* belief system seemed too narrow.

* * *

Walking back to my hostel, I had a zip in my step, avoiding the cracks and thinking about the Old City bazaars with the Bedouin Nomad jewelry and hand-embroidered fabrics. Tomorrow would be a market day. I would push the nagging thoughts from my mind; the thoughts stirred up by Jon and the experiences I encountered today. I picked up some *falafels* on the way back to eat peacefully in my room. Then I recorded my thoughts in my journal to keep them from whizzing around my brain. After all, tomorrow is another day.

I awoke with the `call' of Old Jerusalem Market, beckoning me to discover what enchanting wares it embraced in its colorful hold. I wasn't into maps; that side of my brain is a bit dormant, so I simply ask questions. When I exited my hostel, I asked a kind-looking man in uniform, "Where street markets?" He replied in perfect, accented English, "I can show you the best; it is the *souq* (Muslim `street bazaar'). My name is Asad Salah, and I'm a local policeman." He told me that the word *souq* derives from a French slang word for chaos. And it was! What a *fiesta* of activity. The market began only a few blocks further up.

We walked down *Helena* Street, skidding on the eroded slick stones laid by the Romans. Helena was the mother of King Constantine, the first Christian King of the Roman Empire. As the street narrowed, we had to dodge the cages filled with singing birds, candy shops, shawl shops, jewelry displays, food stands, all encroaching onto the narrowing path. My self-appointed guide had a word with each shop keeper. They waved or nodded, "*As-salaam 'alykum*, peace be upon you." I presumed my guide was a 10% hustler since cops were not well paid. However, I was pleased to have a guide that also served as a body-guard.

The receptionist at my hostel warned me, with a pinched face, "Don't show your knees or shoulders." I had a zany image of all the women on the street with only their knees and shoulders covered and the rest *au naturel*. I wore the same sober outfit from yesterday – long jeans and my long-sleeved white blouse with my hair pulled back and constrained. I wished I had worn a veil since we were majoring on the Muslim quarter.

We had to jump into a candy shop to make way for a group of pilgrims following a man carrying an oversized wooden cross. Asad explained, "*The Via Dolorosa*, with the stations of the cross, weaves through the Muslim quarter." He pointed to the 7th station and said the devout Christians trailing behind were from the Orthodox Church of Greece. We were at the crossroads of a culture-collision, and no-one was bothered.

A piercing voice boomed sharply from various loudspeakers, calling *the faithful* Muslims to prayer… …or else they would be condemned to that piercing, droning voice throughout all eternity. I guess the locals became numb to the audio-intrusion, or else deaf.

I questioned Asad about the proximity of the four quarters of Old Jerusalem. "They touch one another - the Christian quarter is in the northwest corner, leading to the Holy Sepulcher Church. In front of us, straight east, is the Muslim Dome of the Rock Mosque. Directly opposite, to the west, is the Jewish Wailing Wall and the Temple Mount. The Armenian quarter is in the southwest tip through Zion Gate."

I casually asked Asad if he knew someone who sold items from the Bedouin Nomadic Tribes, living in the Israeli Negev Desert. I discovered nomads always had the best stuff, as far as ethnic jewelry and embroi-dered items go. Asad's eyes lit up, and he exclaimed, "Of course, my friend Mustafa has the best collection in town."

"Is he very far?" I questioned Asad. "No, he's just around the corner." "Yea, can we go now?" I insisted. "Of course, but first, you must try the best hummus in Jerusalem. It's made of the tastiest chickpeas with at least 30% *tahini* (sesame seed paste). Dip some of this freshly made, hot pita bread in and take a scoop. Being a policeman had its perks - Asad was offered something at most of the stalls. Coffee, tea, birds, sweets, whatever they were selling. He politely refused until we arrived at the Hummus Bar.

The Bedouin shop was a dream. I wanted one of everything but set-tled on a brightly beaded maiden's wedding cap and an embroidered dress that would literally stop traffic. I also craved a fedora hat like the Jewish Orthodox men wear, resembling the Códovan hat worn by eques-trians in southern Spain, crafted in Córdoba. Asad said we'd have to go back to the Jewish quarter for that accessory. I found an excellent copy of the Italian made Borsalino and was advised by Asad to wait and wear it in another country. I took his advice.

Skipping back to my hostel, Asad politely asked me, "Madam, will you please walk? It is more dignified." Ah yes, I had to think about his image in the neighborhood. He reminded me, "Only children skip in our country." I thought about it for a minute and realized that only children skip in my country also. But I was an atypical young adult. I felt like Peter Pan's cohort, Wendy. I had a Never Never Land philosophy. Peter Pan said that you could fly when you think happy thoughts, and that's a prov-en fact - at least mentally and emotionally. I might get older, but I certainly didn't plan on growing up.

* * *

I kept having flashbacks of the events of yesterday. It was too much to digest, so I had to push it out of my mind. On the one hand, it was too awesome to believe that the Creator of the Universe would single me out and actually speak to me and appear to me in the form of a blinding white light.

Remembering Luke's verse, "Seek and you will find," gave me comfort. Well, I had been seeking, but I was not sure if I really wanted to find the Truth. The TRUTH came with responsibilities. I mean, everyone has a purpose in life and perhaps mine is to search. Jon told me that God must have a special mission for me.

I pictured myself languishing away in a mud hut with a thatch roof in some village in Africa, where I had to walk five miles a day to get a jug of water to carry back on my head, to share with the villagers. I knew I couldn't hack that sort of sacrifice. I wasn't sure if I could change my quirky ways. What if I had to wear normal clothes? Like a high neck blouse with a lacy collar and a knife-pleated skirt that extended below my knees. Ugh, what if I had to wear sensible shoes and stockings with neat pumps? If I believed in Jesus, the anointed one, would I have to tame my hair?

Mark Twain said, "Never put off till tomorrow what you can do the day after tomorrow." That had become my motto. I decided the best thing about the future is that it comes one day at a time, so I could handle that. I would wait for God to direct my path and pray that it didn't require too much change or challenge.

Now that I knew my way around, I would spend tomorrow retracing my steps and visit the Jewish and Armenian shops. I also wanted to return to the Wailing Wall and stick another prayer request between those ancient stones. I would grab some *falafels* and finish off the fruit I had in my room and catch up with where I left off in my journal.

It was a joy to wake up to another glorious day. I looked forward to visiting the famous Mahane Yehuda Market. It was partially covered with a transparent roof that allowed the sun to pour in and set the myriad of tantalizing goods aglow. The atmosphere was like an amusement park. Everyone was having a good time - it was a comfort zone of smiling people.

Heading back to the Wailing Wall, I wedged my new prayer request between those holy stones and rocked it up to heaven, swaying from the waist, front to back, like the Orthodox Jews surrounding me. I admired their devotion and being encircled by their prayerful wails. I hoped that today would be the day they would have a revelation of prophecies in their Torah about Jesus being the Messiah. It gave Jon such a "rush," I was sure that it would also enable them to see the world in 3D, living color instead of the black and white, which they wore so religiously.

I was getting fidgety to get back to Rome. I already knew the shops I would head to that would love my eclectic variety of treasures. There would be work opportunities also – I'd check in with a modeling agency that a friend recommended a year ago when I was last in that `anything-goes city.' I had spent nearly a month there and knew my way around. I had walked every street and lane within a mile of the Spanish Steps. I could finally check into the American Express office, which had become a world-wide post office for American tourists.

After a repeat stroll around Old Jerusalem, re-visiting the holy shrines and taking in vibes of the ancient cultures, I slinked back to my room, pink panther style, re-centered myself, and meditated on the earth-moving events of the past three days. I started with my mantras and breathing exercises, then zipped on to some yoga, finishing up with a good, thorough cleansing of my chakra points. However, I sensed that something was amiss; I didn't have the same fulfillment with my daily routine. I had done my Sun Salutation morning greeting, but there was a gnawing absence of something else. Oh well, some days are like that. I'd think about it later. I repacked the array of stuff strung around my room so I'd be ready for my early flight in the morning.

16. ROME

Wearing my opportune travel outfit, as usual, I looked forward to the contrast of over-friendly, light-hearted, somewhat frivolous Romans. My flight was at 9 am on Israeli Airlines, *El Al*, and as I entered the aircraft cabin, I became aware that 99% of the passengers were Italian. It had to be a package-tour group because everyone knew each other and were yelling across the aisles and sitting on the arm-rests. Half an hour into the flight, the decibel count of the unruly passengers was off the charts. I was convinced, at any moment, a sonic boom, signaling the breaking of the sound barrier, would rip through the plane, knocking us out of our seats.

I warmed to Italians – they were gregarious, extroverted and exaggerated. I could relate to their social graces in controlled doses. The flight would be about four hours. With paper stuffed into my ears, I started to sing, to block out the roar of the masses. "I'm leaving on an airplane, la-la-la. . ." I couldn't remember all the lyrics, so I kept repeating Peter, Paul and Mary's partial lament until my throat was dry.

My chakra energy-points were contracting, and my third eye was closing. I was reaching my sanity limit. I resorted to staggering around in the cramped ladies toilet for the last half hour of the flight, to have some peace until the "fasten your seat belts" sign started flashing, forcing me back to my seat.

We landed at the Leonardo da Vinci Airport amidst cheers and shrill whistles. Ah, back to `The Eternal City.' After all, Rome's history spans twenty-eight centuries and is one of the oldest, continuously occupied cities in Europe. Every block of the city flaunted its breath-extracting beauty and esthetic, ancient past. I was in the Romans' homeland, the metropolis of one of the greatest empires in classical antiquity and one of the world's most visited cities.

Exiting the plane, I wore my black Orthodox fedora hat to make a splash upon arrival. Hats can make or break the wearer – they were my 'tour de force.' They gave me a classy oomph. It seems the hat also brought me a group of fans, pen in hand, begging for my signature. Rome's airport was known for its 'autograph groupies' that hung out at the exit ramp, waiting to identify someone famous. They looked at me and started screaming, "Oh Carly, we just love your new hit, "You're so Vain."

When I previously admitted I was only Carly Simon's look-a-like, people thought I was lying and giving them the cold shoulder. So to protect Carly's reputation, I smiled, signed the singer-songwriter's name and said, "Have a good day and keep singing." Carly Simon was alarmingly talented but certainly not beautiful; however, she had style and a unique appeal.

My *fans* were confused when I jumped into a battered taxi rather than a limousine, and I waved farewell to them with regal aplomb. I directed the driver to deliver me to Hotel Sorisso, near the Spanish Steps. The square was a popular place for artists, poets, pick-pockets, and gigolos. The well-dressed, gallant young men preyed on American tourists, armed with lethal charm and good looks.

Having spent nearly a month in Rome before heading East, I knew very well the slippery ropes. When I questioned a local about the quantity of gorgeous, captivating men in the area, I was told: ugly men have to get jobs, while those born beautiful earned more by "working" the female tourists. American Express was next to the Spanish Steps, so it was the perfect spot for scam artists of every flavor to stake their territory. I thought, well, it takes two to tango - I was not so naïve.

My well-worn little hotel, *Sorisso* (Smile), was in the center of the elite neighborhood, *Tridente*, plus it was also a short ramble to almost every place of interest. Within two miles, you had the fountain of Trevi, Plaza de Navona, the Colosseum and Forum, the Vatican, Sistine Chapel, the Pantheon, plus a ton of cafes, clubs and eateries.

The city's designer-shop center was also nearby, up and down Via Veneto plus all the cross streets within a six-block area. The chic Romans did their shopping here also. The elegant locals stood out amongst the sport-shoed, informal American wealthy.

The Italian ladies were a far cry from the film version of the plump, haggard housewives in their stained frocks, sporting an apron saturated with olive oil and tomato sauce. They were always portrayed as living in their kitchens, cooking up colossal pots of spaghetti, while shouting at their ten snotty-nosed *bambinos*. On the contrary, Rome's luxurious ladies were on par with the posh French females, in shape and style.

The location of my hotel more than compensated for its modest, meager amenities. I unpacked my suitcases and sorted out my "for-sale" items and samples. I wanted to get to work and hit the `movie-star-shops' for some quick sales. My funds had whittled down to $30, igniting my ambition.

* * *

I had to psyche myself up to visit Mama Lula's swanky shop. I knew she would love my stuff, but she drove a hard bargain. In Rome, haggling was a way of life, whether for purchasing a lemon or a Lamborghini. It was considered `fair play' to cheat or even steal, which was recognized as shrewd negotiating. I had met Mama Lula at a dinner party nine months ago, and she asked me to come to her first when I returned from my travels in the East, loaded with goods.

Lula looked like the mechanical, alabaster, fortune-teller who sat permanently in a tall wooden box in the Penny Arcade back home. She had the same red ringlets, large gold hoop earrings, over-rouged cheeks, and a fake beauty-mark punctuating her chin. You expected her to whip out her crystal-ball and tarot cards at any given moment.

Her shop re-opened at 4 pm, so I was the first to enter. "Hi Lula, re-member me, the American friend of Paolo, who was off to the Far East last July? Well, I'm back with some out-a-sight items from eight coun-tries." Lula's eyes opened wide, "Hello, darling; I love your hat. How could I forget you? You're the young lady with legs up to her armpits and a ton of hair, with rainbow-colored streaks. Let's see what you have."

Artistically, I spread out about twelve embroidered items and my sil-ver serpent belts. I could see her eyes dart to the belts, and she almost started to drool. However, she appeared nonchalant – that was part of the game.

"I'm overstocked at the moment," she replied. I read her technique, "No problem, Alba told me she wanted to buy whatever I brought back," I replied. I started to fold up my embroidered beauties. "Wait, I can al-ways buy for the future if you make me a good price," retorted Mama Lula. I told her the prices, doubling what I wanted.

I hoped to get about tenfold my purchase price. After all, I had to cover the airfare, hotels, food, etc. The drama continued until we agreed on the price that I had in mind. She also took some orders on my silver belts. Lula tried to offer me a price I couldn't refuse for the belts, but I needed to show them as samples to other contacts.

Lula smiled but remained seated. I folded up the two remaining piec-es and announced, "Hey, one shawl is missing." Mama Lula pretended to be surprised when she stood up and realized she was sitting on it. I gave her credit for craftily trying to steal the shawl, but it was all part of the game. I had a pocket full of money to keep me going until I found work.

* * *

I would drop by Alfa Modeling Agency; it was near the "in" Piazza del Popolo Plaza, an easy jaunt. I stopped to have a snack at the renowned café in the center of the square, Bar Canova. A few of the regulars were having sundowners while it was still bright daylight. Roman Polanski stood up and invited me to have a seat. He shared his table with the aging fashion designer Oleg Cassini and his brother Igor, better known as Ghi-Ghi. They were part of the crowd in which my Italian friends hung out. Because they were the older set, I sat down to be polite. "And where have you been Miss Sunshine?" asked Ghi-Ghi.

Playing my Bali card, I then retraced my travels. They seemed impressed, and the Cassini brothers invited me for dinner at 9 pm, but I explained I'd just flown in from Israel and wanted a quiet evening. Oleg added, "Remember, I need girls to model my new bikini collection if you're interested. The shows in Milan start in a few weeks."

"Thanks, I'll see if it fits into my schedule. I'll let you know." He could always be found at Bar Canova. Oleg, with his thick, silver hair, was still riding the wave of fame as the ex-husband of Gene Tierney and the exclusive designer for Jackie Kennedy. Federico Fellini and Marcello Mastroianni were regulars when in town; however, they were all elderly, as far as I was concerned.

I wasn't looking for a permanent job or any sentimental attachments. My goal was to return to Nepal within four months, then down to Jaipur to purchase more tribal jewelry for my budding business. My quest was to continue searching and keep traveling. There was still Africa and South America looming before me.

Convinced that marriage was not my "thing," I knew that marriage and family represented a significant commitment and too many responsibilities. Too high a divorce rate in my family – it might be hereditary or in my genes. I was happy to be single, footloose and fancy-free. Besides, like Groucho Marx always said, "Marriage is the chief cause of divorce."

* * *

The modeling agency was buzzing, so I clocked that as a positive sign. I introduced myself and left a few photos. They were very friendly and told me I was just the type they were looking for – ha, the usual line. I could tell they were holding back laughter after looking at my unprofessional snap-shots.

"First, you'll need a professional portfolio of photos, and Bruno is the best photographer in town. We'll set you up with an appointment. He won't charge you if you give him carte blanche to use the photos at will." What did I have to lose, "Sure, whenever," I chirped. I gave them a card from my hotel, "Just call and leave a message at reception."

"Ah, do you by any chance know how to water-ski?" the agent asked me. "I was born on water-skies; I thought about making it a career," I exaggerated. "The advertising agency for Evinrude & Johnson outboard motors just called. They need a leggy model who can ski – it's for a pho-to-shoot next week." "Well, I'm your girl," I hurled back confidently. I knew that it would be a piece of cake.

I skipped back to American Express to exchange my surplus Liras for traveler's checks and noticed a classy new boutique, *Angelos*, just across the street. I stopped to see if it was "designer" and if my stuff would fit in. Wow, cool duds, my style, in my dreams. I scrutinized each item until a distinguished man of about 45 asked me in heavily accented English, "May I help you, madam?" "Oh, I'm just admiring your amazing collection – absolutely my style," I cooed.

"Well, my wife and partner is the buyer. She makes all the `shows' and buys what she likes to wear, and it always flies out of the shop. Oh, here's Alona now, returning from the hairdresser." Alona was tall, slim, with an olive complexion, long auburn hair and enormous green eyes. I affirmed, "You are a fortunate man to have such a beautiful wife who also has such good taste." I like to tell the truth, especially when it is a compliment. He then announced, "She was crowned Miss *Bellissima* (Miss Gorgeous) three years ago, but I stole her." Alona glanced over at me and said to her husband, "Hey, what about her?" Alexander said, "Yes, absolutely."

"We have a friend who is a new designer, and we think he will take off `big time.' We believe in him." He then added, "I saw you studying his collection and wondered if you were a copier. We get loads of rip-off artists who copy our designs." "Why no, absolutely not; I'm a model, not a designer." After all, I had done some modeling in New Orleans, so that justified my reply.

"Our friend is called Roberto Cavallini. He will be showing in Florence, and his introductory `shows' are for hand-picked clients." Alona and her husband communicated in English and were having a conversation about me, as if I was an invisible commodity. Alona said, "She looks like she could be Hebrew or Palestinian with a dash of African – the combo Roberto would like. He doesn't want any classical beauties, but some atypical models.

"Since he has the Navajo Indian collection this season, she would fill the bill for that. What do you think?" Angelo glanced at me from head to toe and nodded, "Perfect." He then took a Polaroid photo of me and asked how they could contact me. I gave them my hotel card and took one of their boutique cards.

Why not? I decided to go for it and whipped out my silver belts, "Would you be interested in these silver belts - they're great on a bare midriff." I could read Alona's body language. "Maybe; what price are they?" I gave her my highest price to work down, but she agreed on the first price. I then explained that I was taking orders and would head back to India in four months. She said, "Yes, I'll make an order and work out a deposit." Wow, I didn't even think about demanding a deposit – but that was the smart thing to do.

* * *

I thanked my lucky stars for guiding me into that shop! I also thanked the God of the Universe and his angels for blessing me. Today was the start of my love affair with the Eternal City, *la dolce vita*. `The sweet life' was embracing me, and I was ready for its caress. I seemed to float to the cafeteria that I frequented months ago. It had great salads and the best mozzarella made from fresh buffalo milk. Then I strolled back to my hotel singing..... "Everything's going my way....la-la-la."

Now, I only had to let the dust settle and wait for some phone calls. I'd go to the post office the next day to telephone my cousin Fran in Paris and ask her to send me my suitcase by airfreight. I longed to have my custom made, tight hugging, soft kid leather mid-thigh-high boots, camouflaging my skinny calves and giving some pizzazz to my hot pants outfits. I needed "interview clothes." First impressions are vital for future work.

I'd wait one more day to call Flavio, my gay buddy from Bali, who was co-producer of the Italian production being filmed there. He insisted I should stay with him when I came to Rome, but I knew I had to play my cards right and not appear desperate. It was more subtle to call from a hotel rather than a bus depot. I would also be able to announce I had upcoming work modeling. It would be better all-around to have him beg me to stay than to appear needy.

The shops were closed by now, so I decided to go window-shopping and get my bearings for other outlets and see if any new shops had popped up in the past ten months. It was sunny and lots of restaurants and café's had tables on their terraces. I could hear laughter as well as heated discussions reverberating around the tables. But I discovered that Italians loved to have passionate arguments about trivialities. It was a sport. Italians did not eat alone or even in pairs. A table of six was puny; twelve was acceptable.

When I was last in Rome, I explored the meaning of fine dining. You ate, not to simply fill-up and go out to a film or the theatre. You ate for the sake of eating, and social interaction was the goal. Meals often lasted up to four hours, including five courses, plus coffee and a digestive, such as sorbet or grappa (firewater). The trick is to eat small-scale portions, or you'll never get past the starters. I decided on my cheap-o cafeteria; one course was enough and I wouldn't get heckled.

I reflected on my marvelous, productive day and was content to have an early night. I still had one foot in Israel and wanted to catch up with my journal entries, as well as my mantras, breathing exercises and soft-yoga. I decided to also peek into the mini Gideon Bible that Jon gave me to be sure and cover all camps. There was an index listing "needs" and where to find the solutions. Nifty, I hoped it wasn't anything like the I Ching, that Chinese fortune-telling book. I didn't believe in astrology or horoscopes since Libras are skeptical.

After dreaming I was afloat on a blow-up mattress filled with jagged oyster shells, I awoke with the decision to call Flavio sooner than later. My bed had sharp little lumpy bumps, plus it sagged. I realized it would be easier to contact my Bali buddy than to demand a different room or another ratty mattress.

* * *

"Hello Flavio, Marie France calling. Do you remember me from Bali?" "Of course I remember you, darling, the funny hippie who was always singing and dancing and became our yoga teacher." "Yes, that's me." "Well, where are you and when are you coming to visit me? Rome is the best city in the world." "Well, I'm actually here in Rome – I'm staying at a hotel near the Spanish Steps, lining up some modeling work." "*Madonna Mia*! Come stay with me, and we can talk about our delicious time in Bali. *Adesso,* Now!"

Flavio's melodious accent, lapsing into Italian, plus his exaggerated body language, made him a delight to listen to and watch. He was a natural comedian without effort. Above all, he'd be a fun and safe escort –

handsome and gay was the perfect combo for a comfortable, relaxed relationship. "Okay Flavio, you convinced me. Is your address still Via N. Taraglia no. 22?" "Yes, darling, I live in the best part of the city, surrounded by embassies." "I'm on my way; I'll grab a taxi," I fluttered.

I told the receptionist at my 'Smile' hotel that I had some unexpected events and would have to leave immediately. He did not smile but instead slapped my bill on the desk and put an extra charge for not advising him within twenty-four hours. I didn't argue; I was so happy to leave, I smiled. I packed my bags in a flash and was off to a comfy bed, I hoped.

As the taxi neared Flavio's house, I could see him from a distance waving to me exuberantly. He was a handsome man of about 46 who retained a boyish, almost impish look about him. His usual expression was that of a kid planning something devious, like putting a spider in your bed. He was slightly shorter than me. However, I had discovered that Roman men sought tall, foreign women as a status symbol – similar to owning an import such as a Rolex Daytona or an Aston Martin One.

What a warm welcome! Flavio smothered me with a full-strength embrace and helped lug my suitcases into the room, especially prepared. His house shouted, "I am rich and loving it." The neighborhood was elite, and his ivy-covered house stood its ground, refusing to be snubbed by the palatial mansions housing the embassies. He motioned for me to leave my things where they were, "*Adesso*, (now), first take a tour of my home."

The décor was 16th century Italian Renaissance mixed with dramatic 17th century Baroque and a smidgen of rollicking Rococo style. Flavio pointed proudly to a grim, dark oil painting that was downright depressing and announced, "This *Rafael* is an original. My uncle, many times removed, was Pope Julius II from 1503 to 1513.

"This painting was part of the collection at the Vatican, as well as the solid gold sunburst over there." He pointed above the Rococo sofa upholstered in dark red velvet and explained, "My ancestors had to hide the treasures during the World Wars and the way I look at it, finders keepers, losers weepers."

I was spellbound; I didn't know whether to laugh or cry. Flavio obviously borrowed his decorator from Count Dracula. It was a great house to lease out for horror movies or a soap opera about a wayward priest.

While Flavio beamed at his family heirlooms, a hunched-over woman with long grey hair and a large hooked nose appeared with an old-fashion straw broom in one hand. When she spoke to Flavio, only two teeth were visible, and saliva dribbled from the corner of her mouth. Flavio shouted something at her, and she volleyed back with a shriek. I wondered if she had Gremlins caged-up in her separated servant's quarters.

He kindly introduced me, "This is Iseppa, my housekeeper. She was my nanny as a child and has lived with me ever since." I said politely, "Pleased to meet you, Iseppa." I thought I saw her turn her head and spit on the carpet. Flavio hollered again, and I reconsidered all the benefits of my crummy little Smile Hotel - after all, it was so centrally located.

* * *

Flavio curtailed my thoughts by blurting out, "There is a cocktail *festa molto importante* (a very important party) with all the best producers and directors in Rome next Saturday, so I can introduce you around. I am so happy to show off my American hippie houseguest that I met in Bali." Help, he started to talk to me in the third person. He told me to be sure and wear my embroidered bell-bottom hip-huggers, my backless top with mirrors, as well as my ankle bracelets, serpent silver belt, the works. He also insisted I go barefoot. It was as if I was a trophy from his travels. Flavio's house décor and housekeeper started to fade from my thoughts.

One thing was clear: I would have no competition. The cocktail-set in Rome would be decked out in the latest Vogue fashion. Who else will have frizzy hair descending past their gluteus maximus and all my cool ethnic jewelry? I might even start a fashion trend for bohemian-chic. I was up for it. "Sounds like a radical idea Flavio, by the way, can I borrow your phone to let my modeling agency and a few other contacts know that I've changed telephone numbers?"

A tune started to bubble up from the depths of my being as I belted out the lyrics, "Everything's Coming Up Roses!" That Broadway hit made a huge impression on me as a pre-teen…..and when it bubbled up, that meant something great was just around the corner.

I phoned Angelo at his boutique and the German boss at Alfa Modeling Agency, to give them my new contact number. Monika, the boss, gasped, "We thought we'd lost you, I called your hotel, and they said you'd left town. Listen, we have a photo-shoot set-up for you with Bruno tomorrow morning early. He said to bring some shorts, boots, revealing blouses and a change of dresses. He wants you to start the play-off with the movie-star soccer team so that he can do a spread for *Oggi* (Today) or *Gente* (People) Magazines. He does good layouts and has connections all over Europe."

My mind started to race; my boots were in Paris. I'd have to go shopping today and invest in some clothes. "Perfect, great, I'll be ready. Hey, do you think Bruno can pick me up at my friend's house on Via N. Taraglia 22?" I asked. "My oh my, you're well connected in that up-market neighborhood," Monika laughed. "Yeah, sure, he'll pick you up at 9 am sharp."

"But Bruno hasn't even seen me, and I don't know how to play soccer." "Don't worry; you only have to kick the ball and then run around the field with the players for a while. Bruno will transform it into something newsworthy. He saw your snap-shots and said you were a raw diamond and he could polish you up with his miraculous camera lens." "Phew, I'll do my best. Tell him I'll be waiting for him in front of the house at 9 am."

* * *

Flavio commented, "*Mamma mia*, you look *pazza* (crazy). What happened?" "I have a photo-shoot tomorrow and I need some clothes. Hey, can you can show me how to play soccer?" "*Che dici* (what are you saying)?" Flavio muttered. "Never mind, do you know any interesting street markets?" That was my only hope of finding something affordable. "Yes, I know the best, but first, I will take you for a ride around town to see my city."

I had my embroidered jean shorts and my midriff tops, so I only needed some boots and a few dresses. I took a deep breath 2-3-4 and exhaled all negativity 2-3-4. It would be okay; I could do it.

It was only mid-morning, and Flavio was anxious to show me *his* city. He backed his Alfa Romeo out of the garage and I hopped in, raring to go. I survived the traffic chaos in Bangkok, New Delhi, Bombay and Paris, but I had never experienced anything equal to Rome's homicidal motorists.

Roman drivers make four lanes out of two, incorporating the sidewalks and the neutral ground. There are absolutely no rules – stoplights and signs are only decorations, direction indicators in cars are obsolete. The Parisian drivers aim to hit pedestrians, while the Italians don't see them because they're making rude hand gestures to the drivers around them instead of looking at the road. It would be comical if it weren't so scary.

I created a system, whereas Flavio taught me the offensive sign language, and I gave each smutty hand-gesture a number. Therefore Flavio just shouted a number one through five, and I stuck my arms out my window and executed the insult. At least it kept his hands on the steering wheel – unless he spoke to me, using wild, frenetic hand motions, as Italians do. They can't help it; they are very expressive. However, all the drivers had a plastic St. Christopher statue glued to their dashboard to protect them. It seemed to work.

Flavio whizzed by all the ancient landmarks of the city, and I exclaimed, "Oooh, ouuu, ahhh, awww, uhmm, WOW! That was all the vocabulary I needed. I finally popped the question... .... "Where is the street market?" "*Bene bene, ti mostrerò* (ok, ok I'll show you)." Flavio pulled up to a huge street market and told me he would never find a parking place, so I could take my time and then make my way back to his house. That was a great idea; that way I could concentrate. I felt I was in `haggle city,' I knew I'd have to expend a lot of energy, but what the heck.

The market was set up in a vast square - the size of a city block. I passed hardware stuff and second-hand bric-a-brac, moldy books... .ah, I could see shoes in the distance. There were about twelve stands with shoes, and yes, a few boots. As I drew closer to the stand with boots, I was mesmerized by a pair of bright green platform boots with red and yellow lightning bolts stitched onto the sides. They were unique; it was impossible that a similar pair existed in this world or the next.

I was careful to look elsewhere, not to alert attention towards my real intention. I asked the price of three ugly shoes and some slippers. Then I casually looked at the boots and asked in sporadic Italian, "How much are these ugly boots?" I looked at the sole to see if they were as big as they looked. Yep, my size.

The lady at the stand took the bait and replied in sign language that they were half price. "Quant'è? (How much), I asked. In deep thought, she rolled her eyes up and said, for everything, I take only 40,000 lire (about $20). "And only the ugly boots?" I asked. She paused to contemplate, then scribbled on a paper and said the equivalent of $10. I offered $5, and they were mine for $7.

These boots surpassed my wildest dreams. They were GALACTIC boots; I would be able to do ANYTHING while wearing them. I was ready for the soccer match. Now I needed a few "catchy" dresses to round out my wardrobe.

There were heaps of frocks on a nearby table. I pulled out a long, fake-silk chiffon dress that looked 100% real. It had a tiny blue flower motif but still transparent enough to require a body-suit underneath.

More digging, and I uncovered a viscose mini-dress. It had cap-sleeves with a wide ruffle that fell softly over the shoulders. Great, I paid half of the top-price and was heading back to Flavio's, mission accomplished.

I heard some giggles trailing me. I swung around and caught three kids walking in a single file directly behind me. They were humming the theme song from "The Pink Panther" and rolled their feet from heel to toe while swinging their arms, exactly like me. I burst out laughing, and they scattered. It was not the first time kids had mimicked my lanky, bouncy, panther-stride.

* * *

Only two bus connections and I got off a mere block from my destination. I hoped Flavio or his housekeeper was home since I forgot to ask for a key. Flavio flung open the door, *"Ciao bella!"* (Hello beautiful). Show me what you bought. He thought my new dresses were "divine" but told me he would not allow those horrid boots into his house. I chuckled and promised I wouldn't wear them with him.

Flavio was a health-freak, so he agreed on a medley of veggies with grated Parmigiano. He would whip up some *risotto al funghi* (rice with mushrooms). Italians like to do everything together, including cooking. He also tossed a mixed salad with olive oil, extra virgin, and freshly squeezed lemon juice. The meal was topped off with a reserve Chianti Classico.

Flavio wanted to speak about his all-time favorite subject, Bali. He went over every minute detail he experienced on that exotic isle - he was clearly in his element. He spoke, and I laughed. He was better at monologues than dialogues. I was happy to listen.

At 10 pm, Flavio announced, early to bed and early to rise. "*Chi dor-me non piglia pesci*" (You snooze, you lose). I washed up, he dried, and we headed to our respective rooms. Hallelujah, the mattress was perfect. I wrote down the day's highlights in my journal and was pleased that I was ready to be molded by Bruno's lens the next day.

I lapsed into Pranayama, "Yoga breathing," until I felt every cell of my body oxygenated.....2-3-4. I tried meditating on my mind's `white light,' but it was elusive. I moved on to my Tibetan Buddhist mantra, "*Om-mani-padme-hum*." After ten minutes *om*-ing, I felt like my routine was still not complete, so I whipped out my little Gideon guide and scanned the index. Ah, "peace," that's a good topic. Hmm, "In peace I will lie down and sleep, for you alone, Lord make me dwell in safety." (Psalm 4:8)

Wow, what an awesome, comfort mantra. I added it to my nightly collage of spiritualities, and it brought balance. I read in minuscule print that the Psalms were songs sung by King David and others. How very apropos! I would try it softly. My room was at the other end of Flavio's large villa, but I didn't want to disturb him, especially on my first night.

Thumbing through the Psalms of my potent little book, I found a dog-eared page and verses underlined (Psalm 23:1-3). Perhaps it was Jon's favorite. I'd sing it in his honor. First, I'll read it. It has such a poetic composition, even lyrical. Yes, I had a melody surfacing as I sang, "The Lord is my Shepherd, I shall not want, He maketh me to lie down in green pastures, He leadeth me beside still waters, He restoreth my soul, he leadeth me in the paths of righteousness, for his name's sake... " I drifted to sleep, a deep delta sleep and awoke hours later, turned off the lights, and got back into bed to dream of green pastures and still waters.

The alarm sounded at 7 am, but I was already awake, day-dreaming. What should I wear to meet Bruno? I knew I'd have about four or five changes throughout the day, but first impressions are critical. I decided on the floral mini-dress with my red high-heeled sandals. That wouldn't overwhelm him, and he could see how long my legs were, in proportion to my body. I'd wear my hair free, letting it cascade over my bare arms. And yes, a straw hat to top off a spring-time 'look.'

The brewing perfume of Italian espresso pulled me into the kitchen, where it was still steaming on top of the old-fashion stove. I splashed some milk into my inky espresso and buttered some bread to dip into the mix. I then ate a banana for power and longed for some peanut butter, but settled for a hard boiled egg. I guess Iseppa, the housekeeper, prepared breakfast. I hoped she hadn't drooled on anything I was eating.

At 7:30 am on the dot, Flavio commenced his morning exercises in that gloomy living room that reeked of ancient antiques. I couldn't believe it. How is it possible that I would be haunted by the Balinese "Monkey Dance" song of clangs and bongs and shrill incessant, repetitive chants from dozens of monkey dancers? The problem was, I had to cross the living room to get to the guest bathroom. I ran through in a Balinese sarong to express solidarity, but Flavio didn't miss a beat of his frantic work-out. No wonder he was so fit at his age.

Next time I passed a drug store, I'd buy some earplugs. I turned the bathwater on full-force to drown out the mind-fracturing noise from Flavio's monkey chant racket. I streaked back to my room to get dressed and collect the change of clothes I'd need throughout the day. My boots were heavy, but worth their weight in gold.

I carefully glued my upper and lower lashes on, added some eyeliner, lipstick and voila, ready to go. I told Flavio I was off, not to wait up for me. He gave me dual-cheek air kisses, crossed his fingers, and said, "*In bocca al lupo.*" That expression is equivalent to "Break a leg," but means, "In the wolf's mouth." I felt like little-red-riding-hood heading out into a forest of the unknown.

* * *

In anticipation, I was waiting on the lawn five minutes early, and Bruno arrived ten minutes late. He stopped the car, got out, knelt on the ground and dramatically bowed forward from the waist, placing the palms of his hands on the ground repeatedly, until I said, "Basta" (enough) while laughing. He then said, "*Bellisima, scusa sono in ritardo.*" (Gorgeous, I'm sorry I am late). I knew we would have a good rapport. Bruno was about a head shorter than me, with my spiked-heels. He was a bit pudgy but full of confidence. He spoke to me in broken-English smothered with Italian superlatives.

We drove for about twenty minutes to a large park with an ornate fountain, various bronze statues, and flowers that frolicked carelessly throughout the garden, brightening up the atmosphere. Bruno announced that the sun would be at the perfect angle in about fifteen minutes, and he would start the photo-shoot. "We will start with what you are wearing, just follow my instructions and look natural."

That was the tough bit, looking natural in such contrived circumstances. He said it would take about ten minutes to loosen up and not to worry. I had seen famous models on set and tried to mimic their poses.

"Now sit on the edge of the fountain and prop your knee up, '*va bene, perfetto.*' (that's good, perfect). Now twirl, now jump, now take your shoes off and run in between the flowers. Now in the fountain, splash the water with one foot." Bruno graded me with a "*Va bene, perfetto*" after each move. It was very encouraging. I figured the sheer quantity of clicks would produce a few good shots according to the law of averages.

"*Prossimo vestito,*" (next dress) Bruno demanded. I had my one-piece bodysuit on already, so I slipped out of my mini into my maxi silk-chiffon dress with the delicate blue flowers. Bruno whistled with approval, adding, "*Bellisima, bel vestito*" (Gorgeous, beautiful dress). Another thousand clicks and poses later, I begged for a snack. Bruno laughed and said, "Ok, ok, but only a snack. Lunch will be after the *partita di calcio* (soccer match)." It seems the movie-star soccer team didn't want to play on a full stomach, so the game was scheduled for noon. Lunch in Rome was never before 2:00 pm.

Bruno stopped at a café/bar where I downed a Coke, he had several mugs of beer, and we both indulged in heavy-laden pizza al *taglio* (slices of pizza). That was a meal for me. We arrived at the football field, and I looked like I was left over from the night before, with my party dress still intact. I dashed into the ladies' room and exchanged my party dress for my jean shorts. I then zipped up my wonder boots and popped on a mid-riff top.

I strode out onto the football field, straight into a wall of whistles and shouts of, *"Bella, bellisima Amazona."* Just what Bruno had anticipated, I was a head taller than the tallest player. I was handed a football jersey that I slipped over my top – number seven. Standing in the middle of the team while Bruno clicked, I was aware that my legs arrived above their waists.

I felt a bit like Barnum and Bailey's prized freak. I envisioned the headlines of Bruno's article for the magazine, "Amazon Warrior invades Rome and holds Soccer Team hostage, with a ransom demand." The Amazons were the mythical warrior women who were the arch-enemies of the ancient Greeks. From Hercules to Theseus, every Greek hero or champion had to prove his mettle by fighting a powerful warrior queen. Well, if they wanted a fight, they were going to get one; I had on my ga-lactic boots!

Little did they know, soccer was a girls' sport in the US, and I knew the rules and tactics. I wasn't the best on our high-school team, but I could hold my own. I was given the kickoff, and I aimed for "kingdom-come." WHAM, my boots must have had steel toes. The ball almost flew over the opposition's goal post.

There was a medley of gasps, including my own. Bruno was running around the field clicking - he looked like an overweight "roadrunner." I tried to maneuver the ball away without fouling or allowing the ball to touch my hands. After about ten minutes, the whistle blew and I was called out of the game. "Shucks," I declared. Bruno exclaimed he had enough shots, and the game would continue without me. Oh well, I wasn't fond of working up a sweat anyway. The team whistled and applauded as I sauntered off the field. I turned around to throw the players kisses from afar – it was the least I could do in exchange for de-railing their game.

It was 1:30 pm when Bruno pulled up to Flavio's house. He explained that his mother would have lunch on the table at 2 pm on the dot, and he couldn't be late. Bruno must have been at least thirty-five, but I realized that most unmarried Italian men still lived at home until they could find a mama-replacement.

Bruno said, "By the way, I need you to sign this release. `Ti render famosa' (I will make you famous)." "Yeah, but first I want a copy of the best photos for my modeling portfolio. That's what my agent told me." "Oh, did she? In that case, I will. *Per favore*, sign here." "First my photos, Bruno, Libras are skeptical." I blamed my lack of trust in my zodiac sign. Bruno looked wounded, shrugged and replied, "*Va bene* (okay), day after tomorrow, they'll be ready....and then you will sign?" "Of course, call before you come, and I'll be ready." Bruno smiled, "*Ciao bella.*"

Bruno kept his word; he delivered the photos as promised. I signed the release and prayed I wasn't signing away my very life. My agency was right; he had a miracle lens. He made my nose shorter, my eyes larger, my cheekbones higher, and my legs longer. It was hard to believe it was really me—there were no touch-ups, only the perfect lens, angles, smoke and mirrors. Bruno was a master at his craft.

17. MISS EVINRUDE

Monika from the agency called the following day to let me know that the Evinrude-Johnson advertising team saw Bruno's photos of me, and I had been chosen. I would become "Miss Evinrude Outboard Motor Girl for 1973". They were working in advance, of course, and would start shooting the following day. I looked forward to going water-skiing, and I had several cute bikinis to show-off.

"Be ready at 6 am," Monika informed me. "6 am?" I contested. "There's better light in the morning, and it takes half an hour to get to the lake," Monika explained. "OK, what's the pay?" "Beginners' fee, $20 an hour." Rip-off agency, I thought. On the other hand, it might open doors for opportunities if being `Miss Evinrude Outboard Motor Girl' had any prestige at all.

This Saturday was the big cocktail soiree chock full of producers and directors, according to Flavio. At least I'd have something to boast about, which I accomplished here in The Eternal City.

The Evinrude team agreed to pick me up at Flavio's place at 6 am - everyone was impressed with my chic address. In any case, I'd escape the frenzied Monkey Dance noise that Flavio started punctually at 7:30 am - small mercies.

On the stroke of six, the van pulled up towing the ski boat, equipped with a spanking-new Evinrude outboard motor. It would be great for powering speed to jump the wakes and slalom in style. I hopped out of the van next to the dock, and I was glad I brought my jean jacket; it was nippy. One of the team handed me a legless wet-suit and said, "You'll need this; just put it on over your bathing suit." Uff, my bikini would be swallowed up in orange neoprene.

I jumped into the boat with three guys. There was the driver, a male model with full neoprene, who'd pretend to go deep-sea diving, and another man in a bright red wet-suit who was the photographer. Wow, the slalom ski was fantastic, wooden Kangaroo mahogany – the best. The captain zoomed to the middle of the lake, cut the engine and said, "No life-jacket, better photos." I nodded in agreement – I was a seasoned swimmer and did not need one. Yes, it would spoil the effect. "Jump," he ordered.

Trying to `think' warm, I jumped into the friendly-looking lake, but it was a frigid monster trying to devour me. Until I became numb, I couldn't speak or breathe. I had never experienced such a sharp, cold shock. It was off-season and quite a chilly spring – my plummet felt like a polar plunge.

The crew tossed the ski to me and then the rope. The bar was wooden; I needed neoprene gloves, so my fingers wouldn't plink off like fractured icicles. I adjusted the ski and arranged the rope and screamed, "HIT IT." Nothing. The three guys were laughing and drinking coffee from their thermos flasks. One guy waved to me. Meanwhile, I had to tread water the entire time - at least it kept my blood from freezing.

I screamed again. Nothing. I made the rude hand gestures that Flavio taught me when we were in chaotic traffic. They pointed at me and laughed as if I were a vaudeville show. I started to pull myself in towards the boat with the ski rope and the driver screamed, "Aspetta, partiamo adesso" (wait, we're leaving now.) I yelled, "ADESSO (NOW), or I quit."

Vroom, the motor started up with a jerk while the slack in the rope disappeared, and I was up. I screamed, "FASTER you bums, full throttle." I wondered if the breeze against my face and legs was covering me in frost.

What exhilaration, I sped as far out to the right as I could, then shifted my weight and leaned to the left, flying over the wakes and swinging wide outwards, then back to the right again. I kept up the pendulum effect while my adrenaline-release fed the rush from my numb toes to the goose-bumps on my scalp. *"Whoa! I feel good...."* Come on, James

Brown, let's boogie! I did a little squiggle in between the wakes.....
"YES ... I feel good .... YOWW!"

Captain Know-Nothing slowed the engines, and I started to sink. I
kept motioning for him to speed up. No luck. He pointed to the guy going over-board with tanks and gestured that he had to take photos of him.
I swam towards the boat to get in, but they said, "*No, non ancora*" (no,
not yet). We need two more takes. Better with more light," said the photographer. "We just needed to test the boat."

They gave me some hot coffee from the side of the boat but wouldn't
help me in. I started to pray, focusing on my breathing, did both sets of
mantras, and spoke soothingly to my chakra points. I couldn't afford to
have my energy points shut down on me. I needed a surge of power to
execute two more skiing exhibitions. I fought off hypothermia by tread-
ing water.

Hallelujah, I did it. I rose to the occasion with the help of my higher
power. The photographer got the shots he wanted, but I was shriveled up
and water-logged. They dropped me back off at Flavio's house at about
noon. I was still shivering. Flavio opened the door and shrieked. "You
look terrible, and that blue lipstick is not a good color for your complexion." All I could say was, "I'm cold." I limped in and shuffled to the bath
and turned on the hot water until it steamed and fell into the tub and remained there until I thawed out. Flavio kept running around in circles
screeching, "*Non morire, non morire*" (don't die, don't die). "*Non voglio la
polizia qui*" (I don't want the police here).

* * *

Yeah, I was looking forward to the hot-shot cocktail party and the impression I would make on those producers and directors. Flavio fluttered
around me, making sure I had dressed the part, so he could show-off
what he found in Bali. I don't think he was concerned about my career or
the finances I needed to fund my next exploits. I dressed to the hilt – all
my tribal jewelry and lots of ivory-bone bangles. My woven, beaded

headband, mirrored, backless midriff top, embroidered jeans. Flavio insisted I go barefoot and jangle with ankle bracelets. Of course, he dressed designer-classical.

The party was held at a well-known producer's villa about twenty miles outside of Rome. There was a butler at the door who bowed as we entered. Flavio was in hog-heaven. He received the response for which he'd hoped. All eyes were on us as I looped my arm into his for a sense of security. The women looked furious because they'd spent a fortune on their designer ensembles, and everyone was looking at the hippie.

I looked like a three-ring circus—something for everyone, plus a little left-over. I told Flavio to tell them I was a model, and this was the new look – bohemian chic. The elegant ladies figured they had missed the mark. They all had on versions of the same outfit that graced the cover of that week's Vogue Magazine – a Yves Saint Laurent pin-stripe masculine suit with a white silk blouse. . . .so boring. Flavio and I were the "it" couple, something novel, not afraid to break with protocol. I was introduced to all of Flavio's friends or 'wannabe' friends.

Champagne and canapés were being served while the band struck up a jitter-bug number. I took Flavio's hand and twirled him under my arm, and we took off. Boy, could he jive – I knew Flavio was fit, and jitterbug was his era. I was a youngster when jitterbugging was at its height, but I could follow. He slid me between his legs and back up again, then onto one hip, and alternated to the other. I felt like a limp Raggedy Ann doll being tossed around. I didn't realize Flavio had the strength to flip me about so effortlessly. He was in his element.

An American producer introduced himself as Brent and asked me from which state I hailed. Flavio had warned me not to give too much away and to remain mysterious – so I was vague. He wanted to know if I had experience acting, and I replied, "I've been acting since I could breathe." I exaggerated my southern drawl. "Do you know how to ride horses and shoot?" he asked. "Of course, I was born on a horse, and I've had to shoot my way out of the South."

He laughed and said, "I think you're right for the part. I'm looking for a young lady to play the rogue, saloon keeper - she hangs out with the bad guys of Cheyenne. Not a sweet, curvy type, someone with character who can keep up with the guys - someone who epitomizes self-sufficiency." "Sounds like me, alright."

Brent was just one of the dozens of producers, directors, and actors who jumped on the band-wagon, heading to Rome to capitalize on "Spaghetti Westerns." Clint Eastwood's *Dollars Trilogy* was released in the US in 1967. It went big-time, and Clint became a house-hold name over-night. First, *A Fistful of Dollars,* then *For a Few Dollars More,* followed by *The Good, the Bad and the Ugly,* with the haunting background-score of Ennio Morricone's howling wolf, eerie whistle, flute and evocative choir. Sergio Leone became the king of directors.

Of course, Brent wore custom-made cowboy boots and a Stetson cowboy hat. He was an Eastwood look-a-like, with a softer expression. "Would you like me to try out for the part?" I asked. "No need, you fit the bill. You're exactly what I envisioned," replied Brent. "Up until now, I couldn't find that savage quality you emanate."

My brother and I had horses since we were kids and galloped around the countryside with exhilarated freedom. But to tell you the truth, I nev-er really felt comfortable on a horse, and the horse knew it. I'd get tossed frequently. But never-mind, I'd put on a good show. My brother often took me bare-back riding, and I hung onto him as he whizzed through the forest with finesse. However, when he ducked for low branches, he forgot to advise me, so I also learned to fall off a horse with expertise. That might come in handy.

I asked Brent when he planned on starting the film. He laughed and replied, "Next week, I was waiting to find the right female lead. I have the rest of the cast, cameramen, makeup and wardrobe crew on hold." "Do I need to sign a contract?" I wondered. "Naw, we use the honor code. You'll just have to sign a release."

He also mentioned, "By the way, can you dub?" "Of course," I said matter-of-factly. "We won't record the voices until afterward. You'll speak, but then dub the words in later in the studio." "Okay, it's a deal." We shook hands.

Brent gave me his card and said they would be filming at Cinecittà, the 99 acres studio, considered the Italian cinema hub. It was only six miles from Rome's center and was regarded as the most significant pro-duction community in Europe. Worldwide, it was second only to Hollywood.

I introduced Brent to Flavio and he smiled and said, "We know each other well." Flavio winked and said to me, "Be sure you get paid first." They both laughed. Brent said he'd call Flavio when the starting date was confirmed…..but definitely within a week.

On the way home, Flavio explained that the Italian government was subsidizing up to half the film costs to encourage the up-and-coming industry. So, producers, directors, actors and crews were pouring into the city. I acknowledged that I always seemed to benefit from "perfect-timing."

Annie Oakley, the famous cowgirl and sharpshooter, was my childhood idol. Now I had a shot of becoming an infamous cowgirl, yeehaw! Annie began trapping before seven, shooting and hunting by age eight, and supporting her siblings and her widowed mother. I only toted an air rifle that fired BBs, but later I had a Smith & Wesson J-frame revolver that I carried in the glove compartment of my big-blue-Buick, only for self-defense. Life in Louisiana was precarious. Amen.

* * *

Flavio informed me that he would take me to mass the next day, Sunday, at 10:30 am. I figured, `while in Rome, do as the Romans do.' I wondered if he was concerned for my soul or if he just wanted company. We would go to his favorite church – the Pantheon. Built-in 124 AD for King Hadrian as a Temple for the Roman gods, it became a Christian church in the 7th Century. Flavio was proud to say that the church had been in continuous use since then. That sounded convincing. Maybe we'd get a coupon for a short cut to heaven by being covered by those centuries of prayers. It couldn't hurt.

Not having church-clothes, I made do with a Balinese sarong that I encouraged to drape to my ankles and wore my nun-type blouse. I had a small scarf for my head. Flavio wore his classical designer church outfit

194

and purposely fasted from breakfast. Penance, I guess. He explained that he was an altar boy in his youth in northern Italy and never missed mass.

Somehow I felt that we were imposters - Bonnie and Clyde attempting to earn brownie-points with The Almighty by turning up for mass after an over-indulgent evening. When my mother reached her wits-end, she would threaten me, "If you do that again, God will punish you." So, I was always a bit on edge.

We entered the imposing, massive temple/church with a solemn reverence, and I mimicked Flavio as he dipped two fingers into the holy-water and splashed the sign of the cross across his pious face and chest. At this point, he had transformed into a saintly monk - he was unquestionably devout. We genuflected in unison, making the sign of the cross, and entered a pew. I thought I saw the reflection of a neon light projecting from my forehead, flashing S-I-N-N-E-R onto the glossy, bald-head of the guy sitting in front of me.

After following Flavio's actions throughout the service, he then motioned for me to tailgate him to the altar for The Eucharist. I was warned by my Catholic friends back home as a youth that it was a cardinal sin for a non-Catholic to indulge in Catholic Communion. Therefore, I hung behind until Flavio glanced at me with an unforgiving gaze. On the long, slow route up to the altar, I felt like a lamb being led to the slaughter. I wondered if I would be struck by a bolt of lightning or, worse, refused by the priest. Would he notice I had Protestant roots?

On the other hand, if God was a God of love, this Sacrament wouldn't bring cataclysmic consequences onto my soiled soul. I prayed. I was raised on mafia films, where the mob heartlessly cut-down their competitors with machine guns, then dashed to the nearest church to confess their dastardly deeds to a priest. The priest mystically forgave all until the next slaughter, and then the process was repeated. I had a vision of Lucky Luciano and Vito Genovese sitting in confessional booths, slipping the priests' hundred dollar bills to make sure they skipped purgatory.

I must admit, although I didn't understand mass, there was a hallowed atmosphere in this ancient church, where perpetual prayer to The Almighty had taken place during the past one thousand four hundred years. On my way up to the altar, I saw the glow of two humongous figures, reaching up to the lofty dome. I wondered if they were angels, but they didn't have wings. I hoped they weren't fallen angels.

Flavio explained that the tombs of the famous artist Raphael, the unknowing benefactor of the pinched painting hanging on his living room wall, and several Italian Kings and poets rested within this vast structure. His only complaint was that the mass was now in Italian, rather than Latin. I was impressed that Flavio was a Latin scholar. However, he confessed that he didn't understand a word of Latin. He just preferred `tradition.' I guess listening to mass in a language you don't understand helps avoid any uncomfortable insinuations. Flavio's enigmatic personality fascinated me. We headed home again for lunch. I couldn't wait to peel off my "church clothes" in exchange for something comfortable that didn't have an overpowering odor of incense.

* * *

Being in the right place at the right time is vital. There was a multicolored tapestry of opportunities for the taking, and I jumped onto the bandwagon with abandon. Flavio called me to the phone, and with his hand over the receiver, he whispered, "Angelo."

"Hello Angelo, Marie France here." "I called to let you know, Roberto Cavallini wants you to do his fashion show in Florence, then on to Paris, for the Pret-a-Porter fashion week. I sent him the Polaroid photo I snapped of you, and he said he trusts my opinion, especially that of my beautiful wife, Alona. So you're `in.' It's a month from now, but mark it into your diary."

"Great, done!" I replied with enthusiasm. "But remember," said Angelo, "He's just starting out, so the pay isn't great, only $100 a day, but travel and hotels are included." ONLY $100 a day? My brain was doing somersaults. That's enough for a Russian Aeroflot flight from London to New Delhi. "That's okay, Angelo. I'll do him a favor since he's new at the game."

I marveled. The prophecy of my Jewish medical-student/artist pal Rise, back in New Orleans, was being fulfilled. And, I didn't even need an interview or to embellish my non-existing modeling career. It would work out perfectly time-wise with the wrap-up of my Spaghetti Western. I would be eliminated by a Winchester Saddle Ring carbine rifle after three weeks of filming. What a classy way to go. And just in time for fashion week in Florence and Paris!

18. SPAGHETTI WESTERN

The filming was starting in three days, and there was absolutely nothing I could prepare. I read the script, the same plot as usual, and I didn't have to memorize it since it would be dubbed afterward. It would be a low-budget film, so I didn't expect a windfall, but it was a start. I was taught to be sure of hitting the target, shoot first, and call whatever you hit the target. So I was shooting from the hip in all directions.

The production van picked me up at 5 am to be prepared with make-up and wardrobe by 6 am in the studio and ready to roll the film at daybreak. There were four amusing guys already in the van, and they introduced themselves as Luigi from Naples, Curt from Pisa, Buck from Rome, and Sven from Stockholm.

Terence Hill and Bud Spencer, both Italian, had become a successful Spaghetti Western comedy team by 1967. I recognized that Sven was the spitting image of Terence Hill and Buck looked like Bud Spencer. Luigi looked like the quintessential `bad guy' broncobuster, and Curt was the tall, lanky Clint Eastwood type. Where there was success, there was excess. American sounding names were adopted by the hopefuls, anticipating the next step would be Hollywood.

They greeted me with, "*Ciao bellisima, benvenuto nella terra della magia.*" (Hello beautiful, welcome to the Land of Magic.) They were veteran cowboy actors and had several films under their bullet-laden belts. I would sneak some humorous scenes into my roll to spice it up a bit. I would coax the camera into loving me. I knew my best angles, and I'd make sure the cameramen did also. The director wanted to make a cross between a Clint Eastwood Dollars film and a Hill-Spencer comedy. Let's see if he can pull it off.

Make-up was a bore, and my wardrobe was not as glamorous as I'd hoped for, but the action shots were fun. Needless-to-say stuntmen didn't fit into the budget, so we all did our own stunts, OUCH. I guess they wanted to test my horsemanship, so they gave me the wild grey stallion and asked me, "Do you prefer side-saddle or bareback?" What a choice! I chose bareback and started praying. I called on The Mighty God of the Universe, his saints, the prophets, and hosts of angels. I tried to remember to grip with my knees and not feel anxious since horses smelled fear a mile away. I kept reminding myself that I *was* a galactic gal.

I went straight from walking my sleek grey, high-spirited horse into a full gallop for a dramatic impact. I loved the speed, and I could feel my long hair trailing in the breeze. I held not only the reins, but I clenched fists full of mane and let out a Cheyenne Indian war cry for special-effects. I felt the adrenaline rush and wondered what I could do for an encore. . . .then I heard CUT!

Good timing, my horse had begun to buck wildly. Perhaps I had given him the wrong knee pressure command, but it felt exhilarating. My male teammates gave me a 'thumbs up,' *"Brava!"* (Well done).

In the next scene, I had to wash big Buck from the chest up in a half-barrel-bath. He had on a bathing suit, so it wasn't very racy, but at least I got to wear a saloon-gal outfit. I accidentally snagged a lock of Buck's virile chest hair with my diamond ring, and he let out a yowl. The hair dangled from my ring, and he had a prominent bald spot on his left pectoral. Never mind, the director laughed-out-loud and announced, "Keep that 'take.'"

Then there was a shoot-out that I survived, and I was able to project a convincing grimace while pointing a rifle at the deputy sheriff. I had a full-face close-up before limping away with Ketchup flowing down my right arm. Day-one was a success, and Brent, the producer/director, complimented us on our varied skills.

At the end of week one, I told Brent I needed a weekly paycheck. Flavio had advised me on that strategy. "No problem, you can collect your payment in cash at the office in town." I did, and all looked hunky-dory until the third week. As that was my last week, extracting my payment became as painful as a root canal.

The accountant explained to me that a thousand young hopefuls would be ecstatic to make a film gratis. I was a combination of "really sweet" and "don't mess with me." I wouldn't budge, of course I didn't have a contract, but I wasn't going to sign a release without my final payment.

Once I sat in the office reception while the secretary tried to convince me that the pay-man was out of town. I decided to out-wait him. I knew his wife would shoot him if he didn't arrive home at 2 pm sharp for lunch. He eventually edged out of his office, filled with *vergogna* (shame), and gave me the remainder of my money. I signed the release flamboyantly and blew him a kiss. *"Arrivederci bello"* (goodbye handsome). I wanted to end on a good note. Who knows, I might be back.

How grateful I was to have a week without work before taking off to Florence, so I could center myself again and feed my spirit. I reflected on Jon's last words of wisdom to me in Jerusalem, "It's not about laws and regulations - it's about a relationship with the King. And it's not about your good works. It's about HIS grace." It was a new concept to ponder. I never did anything to hurt anyone intentionally, but on the other hand, I didn't do much to help anyone either. Something to think about. . . .later.

* * *

I had an action-packed week before taking off to *Firenze* (Florence) for Cavallini's fashion show. Flavio suggested we get together with Celeste and her German boyfriend, Hans. He invited them over for cocktails and hors d'oeuvres. I had become close friends with Celeste in Bali since we often tried to avoid the Italian crew's macho banter. She was born in France, but not the usual coquette, arrogant type of Mademoiselle from Paris. She spoke English with a charming accent and was down-to-earth for a starring lady in Rome.

Celeste insisted we join them for a weekend with her good friend Giovanni, in a village about an hour away. She claimed that Giovanni loved to have a crowd around him - typical Italian. Flavio bowed out, but I agreed. Everyone who could leave Rome on the weekend left, so we were engulfed in a ferocious exodus. Celeste was always understated, wearing a simple, well-cut pair of French jeans and a short-sleeved *Esprit* T-shirt. Her boyfriend was drop-dead gorgeous, with black hair and blue eyes, slim but muscular. He adored Celeste.

Giovanni's weekend villa was shared by other family members, but with five bedrooms and a guest house, it was more than adequate for us all. Giovanni was outside by the pool when we arrived. He jumped up to give us red-carpet treatment. He embraced Celeste, then a man hug for Hans, looked at me enthusiastically and said, "*È questo il regalo che mi hai promesso?"* (Is this the present you promised me?) *"No, que cretino!"* (No, silly-boy). I brought you a home-made cake and your favorite wine. We all laughed, and he raised my hand towards his lips and nodded his head respectfully. I had on my jean shorts and galactic boots with a crop top, so he probably wasn't sure what to do with me.

Giovanni was a typical-looking Italian guy. He was my height, with my boots on, dark-complexioned, dark curly hair, large heavy-lidded eyes and an easy smile. Celeste told me that Giovanni was an architect from a well-to-do family and liked to play the role of *El Padrino* (The God Father). He was harmless but wanted to be in charge and needed to be the host. She said he liked people in general, but they'd never seen him in a relationship; perhaps he was asexual. Ideal, I thought.

"You're just in time to help prepare supper," grinned Giovanni. The four of us crisscrossed each other, dodging knives, pots and skillets – only in Italy! When they saw how slow I peeled potatoes, I was given the task of setting the table. They joked about the setting also.

"Aspettare, aspettare" (wait, wait), I'll call my aunt to join us." An elegant older lady in her fifties asked where she should sit, and Giovanni placed her next to me. "She speaks English, so it's easier on us," he smiled. Of course, table-talk was always in Italian, but I didn't mind; I could concentrate on eating without small-talk. The lovely lady introduced herself as Ingrid. She was tri-lingual but politely spoke to me in cultured English.

Ingrid explained that she was useless in the kitchen and would have trouble boiling an egg. I could relate to that and told her I was allergic to kitchens. She said, "If I couldn't act, I don't know how I'd earn a living." I added, "Yeah, I know what you mean."

Every once in a while, she'd translate the topic of the table, but mostly when someone burst out laughing. She was unusually polite and sedate. Starting with *Melone e Prosciutto* (melon and Italian cured ham), then lamb with fresh rosemary, and a huge mixed green salad. All of that was followed by a plate of local Italian cheese, grapes, and Celeste's chocolate cake.

Ingrid asked me what I was doing in Rome, so I boasted a bit about my "Miss Evinrude" job and the Spaghetti Western stint. I somehow got onto the topic of Bali and my travels. She seemed interested and asked lots of pertinent questions. Ingrid offered, "My son Roberto will drop by tomorrow for the day, and he'd love to hear about your travels. He wants to go to Indonesia." "Great, I'd love to fill him in."

Giovanni announced, "*Chiunque per biliardo o carte?*" (Anyone for billiards or cards?) "Hot dog, I'd love to play pool." I saw the table had pockets. "How about American eight ball or straight pool?" I suggested. Hans and Giovanni snickered cryptically, "Are you joking?" asked Hans. "Girls don't know how to play billiards or pool - you might rip the felt." "I'll bet ya' a game." I quipped. "How much?" asked Hans. "$20," I offered. "Okay, you are asking for a beating." Hans retaliated.

First, I checked the cue sticks and chose the straightest one, and chalked it up. We had a game room in our country house with a pool table, ping pong table, player-piano and an Art Deco jukebox with a swivel arm, filled with 45rpm records. I spent every afternoon after school practicing pool to beat the black-leather-jacket and chains guys from the local bars. I scooped up a lot of extra money to splurge on accessories and other necessities. My mother used to say, "Honey, is that the new fashion? Those boys look like hoodlums."

"No mother, that's the latest fashion." "But their hair is so greasy." "Yeah, that's the Elvis-look." I'm not sure if my mom was naïve or if she just used an innocent approach as a guilt-manipulation ploy. Whatever her motive was, it didn't work very well.

I reflected on the hollow satisfaction it would bring me to humiliate Hans and beat him at a "man's" game. I swallowed my pride and back-pedaled. "Err, on second thought, why don't we play cards? We don't want to leave Celeste out, do we?" Hans laughed and called me "chicken," but I felt secure enough not to have to rise to the occasion and show-off. . . . for once.

After more than an hour of foursome cards, I could feel my sugar-level dipping and a banana-split-craving started to grip my nervous system and psyche. "Anyone up for a banana split?" I bellowed. "A what?" asked Celeste. It is an American dessert that's also nutritious. Hans said, "Okay, but I'll split it with Celeste." He was proud of his command of English. I had bought a bunch of bananas at the fruit market, and I knew Giovanni had *gelato* in the freezer. Now to melt a chocolate candy bar and sprinkle the banana boats with nuts. Too bad I couldn't find pecans, so I settled for salted peanuts.

The guys got into a serious game of billiards; Ingrid excused herself and departed, so I caught up with Celeste on her latest film. She also explained she was presently starring in a TV series - playing a female Robin Hood of the Forest. "Cool," I congratulated her. She slurped down her portion of the banana split and admitted, "It was *délicieux*."

* * *

I was curious about the lady sitting next to me at dinner who said it was fortunate she could act; if not, she couldn't support herself. I asked if she'd been in a film I might have seen. Celeste thought for a while and said, "*Casablanca* or *Stromboli*?" I didn't often blush, but I felt my face turning scarlet. I replied, "I can't believe I didn't recognize Ingrid Bergman." I could have kicked myself for bragging about being Miss Evinrude and talking about my Spaghetti Western film. Ugh! I kept thinking, "Play it again, Sam." I guess I had a subliminal message from Humphrey Bogart.

Celeste laughed and said, "Ingrid is a very private person and was certainly delighted that you didn't ask her for an autograph." I realized I was on safer grounds speaking about my travels, especially with people I didn't know. My travels had become my identity. It was something I could talk about with polished savvy and something most others hadn't experienced. It was my territory.

Roberto, the handsome son of Ingrid, arrived mid-morning while we had a swim. As an opener, he asked what language I preferred to speak. I admitted English, without specifying it was my only language, and it existed mainly of American slang. "My mother tells me that you've been traveling in the Far East, South East, and Middle-East this past year. Do you mind if I pick your brain?" he smiled. "You can call me by my nickname, Robertino." "No, not at all; I adore speaking about my travel-experiences. My nickname is Tyke."

I started in Thailand, then Malaysia, Bali and worked my way through Nepal, India, Egypt and Israel. I said, "Stop me when you've had enough." "No, on the contrary, I want to hear more details." Robertino was jotting down key places to visit. There wasn't much interest in my spiritual journey, so I didn't press it. It seemed in Europe, spirituality meant going to church on Sunday, and you didn't speak about it. Whereas on my travels, spirituality was woven into every fiber of people's lives.

Giovanni asked, "Who wants to go to the village?" I raised my hand along with Celeste and Robertino. So the four of us took off on foot; it was only a mile away. We were given baskets and cloth shopping bags, so the purchased food could breathe. It never occurred to me that food breathed. Like every other village, town, or city in Italy, it was a journey into antiquity. We went from one quaint food shop to the next. Supermarkets were nonexistent. Live chickens were sold at the butcher shops, and pigs' feet were slung together, and a goat's head was swinging in the breeze. Giovanni was excited to see there were fresh lamb's tongue and calf's brain. I was adventurous with food, but I just couldn't bear to see it before it was well diffused into a stew or casserole.

Celeste organized all the purchases for lunch, and I was excused from kitchen duty. I volunteered to wash the dishes. I decided to have a good work-out in the pool. I did my thirty laps and then pranced into the sauna to warm up. Ingrid was sitting there *au naturel.* I gave my apologies and did an about-face when Ingrid said; there's plenty of room sit down. I didn't want to offend her by leaving or keeping my bathing suit on, so I self-consciously worked out of my suit and crossed my legs, pretending I did this every day. In Sweden, I heard that family saunas were a regular occurrence.

During lunch, Robertino spoke about his desire to travel. Giovanni mentioned he and an associate were thinking about delivering a Land Rover to their mutual friend, who owned a Safari Park in Nigeria. They were working out the logistics of crossing the Sahara Desert and how much water and food they'd need. Robertino chuckled, "The only sand I want to cross is on a beach, to plunge into the sea." I waved my hand, "Hey, if you want company, I'd love to go." I thought it was a pie-in-the-sky idea – Italians tend to talk a lot.

* * *

It was a relief to have the last few days to myself before going to Florence. I wanted to condition my hair, polish my nails, buff my feet, wax away wayward hair, pluck my eyebrows into arched perfection, and above all, balance my energy points. I couldn't afford to have a short-circuit mid-runway. I discovered singing Psalms worked even better than my Tibetan Buddhist standby chant, *om-mani-padme-hum.* I got a unique "high" I hadn't previously experienced with other chants and meditations. I also started to read the verses Jon highlighted in that mini-marvel Gideon's guide. They always brought me peace. Starting the day with yoga, Sun Salutations limbered me up and pumped some oxygen into my brain.

I decided I'd wear my hippie-garb since that's what I had on when I met Angelo and Alona. The hippie-look was close enough to be called "bohemian-chic," giving my washed-out garments an upgraded label. Since Cavallini's new collection included soft suede with fringe, Navajo

Indian style, I'd pack my turquoise jewelry and perhaps a silver snake belt. My suede headband with coral and turquoise beading would accentuate the Native American appeal. After all, they invented headband fashion, not the hippies. Then I'd scrunch my dampened hair with styling gel and semi-comb it out for more volume – the wilder, the better. I wanted a lioness 'look.'

Flavio said I could leave my over-sized suitcase with him since I'd boomerang back there within ten days or so. I felt driven to touch base with Ibiza, the springboard of my world travels. Charlie and Angie will have returned from Goa, and I could report on Bali to those who inspired me to experience the "last" paradise. Ibiza was special, and I felt special there. With a conglomerate of misfit-dropouts, I felt normal there..... whatever `normal' is.

There was a knock on my door, mid-toenail polishing. Flavio announced, "Telephone call." Was it my agent? Perhaps Brent wanted me to dub? I hoped my modeling job wasn't canceled. "Coming," I hobbled to the phone with cotton balls between my toes. "Hi, Marie France here." "Hi Tyke, it's Spike." "Spike, my brother?" "Do you know another Spike?" I laughed, "Where are you?" I hoped there wasn't a problem back home. "I'm here in Rome; mom gave me your number. We've covered almost all of Europe with Eurail Passes. We'll be here for a few days." Perfect timing I thought, "Great, let's meet up mid-point. How about the Spanish Steps? Give me time to get dressed and catch the bus - how about noon?" "Okay," replied my brother. "Don't get lost." He knew I had directional dyslexia.

Wow, my big brother, my childhood hero, was here in Rome. I allowed my toenails to dry and jumped into my jeans and T-shirt and skipped to the bus stop. Arriving at our meeting point early, I checked my mail at American Express. Ah, what a coincidence, a letter from my brother saying he'd soon be here with his latest squeeze and a couple of friends from New Orleans. How exciting, I swaggered back to our meeting point and saw there was a clump of back-packers. I stood there, gazing around, and someone poked me on the shoulder. "Hey, star-gazer, did you forget what I looked like?" "Wow, it's y`all - I only saw back-packs!" We exchanged hugs all around and had a good catch-up. I hadn't seen my brother for more than a year.

Spike had a sense of humor as off-the-wall as I did, so we exchanged some cryptic, well-meaning, insulting compliments. I noticed when I was speaking – his eyes were fixed on my hairline. Then he questioned, "What's with all that white powder in your hair? Is that the fashion here?" Ugh, I forget to brush out the flea power. I was still paranoid about fleas and lice in my kilos of hair after months of ratty hostels in India and elsewhere. Every time I sensed the slightest prickle on my scalp, I doused my head with flea powder I found in a pet shop. "Oh, that white powdery stuff is a pre-conditioner. The next step is cream. I have some modeling jobs in Florence and Paris, and I'm trying to whip my hair into shape."

My brother was a fearless cross between Daniel Boone and Davy Crocket. He had innate life-skills and know-how. He was far from a hippie, but he decided to go the overland route to India and Nepal to experience more. I guess I was sort of a prima-donna globe-tripper. I wanted the gain without the pain. I preferred long-haul flights, and then I could deal with trains and busses. I was leaving the next morning to Florence, and they were off to conquer the highlights of Rome, so we had some meaningful hugs, despite the backpacks and promises of "See y'all for Christmas."

19. FLORENCE

I bussed back to Flavio's house to finish my corporal improvement plan and pack my smaller suitcase. Flavio offered to drive me to the train station to make sure I got off on time. He was probably relieved to have a rest from my playful antics.

Practicing my breathing exercises on the way to the station helped to prepare me for the uproar that was the specialty of screeching, chaotic train depots. I made it onto the Laser Line non-stop to Florence and secured a window seat for the mere hour and a half ride.

These high-speed trains had a few drawbacks. When a train passed on the parallel track, it created a mighty whoosh-vacuum, and the windows would vibrate as if they might implode, and I would then be sucked out of the train or else plastered to my seat. I couldn't remember which option. However, nothing that titillating happened. There were the usual train-entertainers that ambled from one car to the next.

First was a violinist with a medley from Vivaldi. He sounded superbly professional, and I wondered how he had fallen from a symphony stage into a train car. I gave him a thousand lira (about a dollar) and prayed that he'd find his way back up to a proper platform.

The next entertainer had a good voice, but his guitar was out of tune. I had to intervene. "*Posso accordae la tua chitarra?*" (May I help you tune your guitar?) He said, "What did you say?" The guy spoke with an Irish accent. "Can I tune your guitar?" "Ok, if you think it needs it." I wasn't a great guitar player, but I was good at tuning. I plucked each string while turning the tuner key, tightening and loosening the strings until I got the `right' pitch. I strummed with satisfaction and handed it back. "Here you go." "Thanks." He started again, "*I'm looking over a three-leafed clover... ... *"

"Now, everyone sing along!" I ordered. Audience participation makes people feel wanted and usually boosts tips. The international crowd knew all the words. There was a global mix of Japanese, German, Chinese, French and some back-packing Americans. "Once again, 1-2-3-4, *Well, I'm looking over.......*" Typical, everyone applauded at the end for themselves. However, they all gave the songster a bill or loose change.

The hippie-looking Irishman asked if I'd like to become his official partner, and he'd halve the takings with me. I thanked him for the lucrative offer but told him, "next trip." It takes a lot of courage to go coach to coach singing. I told him to stick to the Beatles songs and encourage audience participation.

I started to wonder what Roberto Cavallini was like and how it would feel to strut down the catwalk in his delicious suede designs. I was told to wait by the taxi stand, and Roberto would recognize me if I wore the same outfit as I did in the Polaroid. It was my good-luck outfit. Even though I wasn't superstitious, it always brought me good fortune.

Fighting my way to the taxi stand, I spotted a big jeep with flashing headlights. A man stepped out and motioned for me to come. As I rambled closer, a lady in the front seat asked, "Are you Marie France?" "Yep, that's me." She introduced herself and the up and coming designer, Roberto. Johanna was German and spoke English with barely an accent. She was friendly, considering her flawless beauty. Roberto asked me how long I would be staying in Europe. "As long as it takes," I answered. That seemed to be the right answer since there were no further questions.

We pulled up to a palace. In Italy, it seems every other building was a palace at one time. The stone facade and massive arched entrance were impressive. Roberto commented, "I was born in Florence and will remain in Florence. It is the best city in the world with the most treasures." He was polite without being gooey, proper without being condescending. I could tell he was serious about his career and didn't want to get sidetracked.

He showed me the large bedroom with a bathroom en suite that I would share with Johanna. He then invited us into the kitchen to explain the proper way to make Italian coffee and announced he had work to do, and we were welcome to help ourselves to anything in the kitchen. He glanced back at me and said, "You've got the right look for my Navajo collection. Alona was right."

* * *

Johanna offered, "Shall we take an afternoon tour of Florence since we'll be working all day tomorrow?" "Hallelujah yeah, I've never been here before." I was wound up about exploring the cultured pearl of a city, considered the Renaissance's birthplace. It was only an hour and a half by train from Rome but seemed like another planet. Much of the architecture was similar, but the locals' behavior was more conventional, certainly less frolicking and not as much drama.

The first stop was Michelangelo's sculpture of David. I squirmed my way through the throngs of tourists, up to the barrier to have a good long look before being ousted by an even pushier tourist. We paced around Accademia Galleria absorbing Botticelli, Titian, and other Masters, and then inhaled the Uffizi Gallery, Pitti Palace and The Dome. Although Leonardo da Vinci lived near Florence for a productive chunk of his life, his most famous works were elsewhere. We then re-charged with espressos at the "in" café, Le Giubbe Rosse, and indulged in people-watching.

I asked Johanna how she knew Roberto Cavallini. Americans are granted a free ticket to intrude and be obtusely nosy – it's even expected. Johanna said she had modeled for Roberto and attended the grand opening of his first boutique, located in Saint-Tropez, only months ago.

During my third week in Europe, I was invited to the Cannes Film Festival on the French Riviera. I promptly ended up in Saint-Tropez, where Brigitte Bardot was still holding court. She single-handedly propelled the little-known sleepy fishing village to touristic stardom when she played the lead role in "And God Created Woman." The `yacht-set' sailed in, and avant-garde resort fashions proclaimed less is more. The topless style was unveiled, and many women decided that they had to keep abreast of the new craze. Curious vacationers made a pilgrimage to this Mecca-by-the-Med to find out if the stories were true. I understood why Roberto chose Saint-Tropez for his first shop.

I dug a bit deeper, "So what's the story on Roberto?" Johanna admitted, "Seems he went to the Art Academy here in Florence, then into textile printing and ramped up his artistic expression by applying paint to textiles in new and inventive ways. From there, he slid into fashion design with the innovation of designing evening dresses made of `glove leather,' applying his exotic prints on them. I'm impressed. He's talented and ambitious – I believe he's going places."

"And how do YOU know Roberto?" asked Johanna. I laughed, "I don't. Some friends of his in Rome have a chic boutique starring his stuff, and they recommended me to him. They said I have a savage-appeal for his new collection." Johanna smiled and admitted, "Well, I agree with them. You don't look like a typical model."

Well, I thought to myself, I was happy to be an atypical everything. Nothing could be duller than to become a run-of-the-mill human being contributing to ho-hum mediocrity. "We'd better work our way back to Roberto's place since the museums will be closing soon, and he might want us to help with supper," voiced Miss Know-it-All Germany. In my defense, I reflected inwardly – beauties are a dime-a-dozen. How many women have a savage-appeal? Better to possess X-factor that turns heads, something unforgettable, a look that challenges. I came to that conclusion as a last resort but discovered it fits me with perfection.

I was surprised to discover that Roberto's adored pet was a large primate that I first met in his spacious living room, lounging around in a cage the size of a small house. I wondered if his pet was the great-grandson of King Kong – he had a gorilla look about him. I guess he was harmless, but I insisted we lock our bedroom door at night – you never know.

Roberto mentioned that he always printed exotic motifs on his leather designs because he figured he couldn't go wrong copying "God's creation." His favorite animal prints were leopard, zebra, snake and giraffe - often combining many patterns, textures, and fabrics into one ensemble. So you can see, my savage looks suited his quirky designs. Birds and feathers were also thrown into his collage of God's creation sensation. Every once in a while, he broke suit and included an off-beat collection such as his Navajo Indian fantasy. Of course, he would sneak some leopard-print panels into the designs, plus a ripple of feathers.

My work would be two-fold; the cat-walk 'shows' for VIP clients and press, plus the mundane exercise of trying on different models for clients. Whatever it entailed, $100 a day made it worthwhile. I'd do my best.

Johanna announced we had to be in bed by 10 pm since she insisted on washing her hair each morning at 6 am – German discipline. At least that would give me time alone to do my yoga Sun Salutations, meditations, and sing a Psalm or two. Breakfast was at 7:20 am - coffee, toast and a four-minute egg. We left with Roberto for the short drive to the showroom at 7:45 am. Phew, we had a clock-work, boot-camp time-table.

* * *

Three other girls arrived one-by-one before the 8 am deadline. We introduced ourselves and had several minutes of small-talk. Roberto reviewed the fifteen outfits he wanted in the show and kept glancing back and forth at each of us models. We would have three changes each. Yippee, I was handed the most eccentric ones. There were three shades of beige, and all designs included fringe, beading, and feathers. The collection was an authentic Navajo style, with some extreme details. Roberto handed me two dresses slit up one side to expose maximum leg and another backless model with a full skirt. The backless-dress had a leopard-print cape I could sling off and drag behind me.

The first dress I tried on fit like a glove, and the supple suede felt like a second-skin. We lined up on the runway, and the music started. Roberto placed me last, which I took as a compliment. The last impression is the lasting one. He had done his homework because the music sounded like the real-deal, recorded at a Navajo pow-wow.

He told us to wait until the person ahead of us made the turn and was heading back down the home-stretch, about three yards from the starting point, before taking off. Then at the grand finale, we'd space about ten seconds between us, wearing the five most spectacular dresses of the collection. We nodded in unison.

The first girl sullenly slinked down the runway with a dead-pan expression. She swung one leg in front of the other with precision, walking in a straight line. She looked extremely professional, but boring. The next three girls followed suit, each looking as if they'd been hypnotized and the muscles in their faces paralyzed, "Return of the Zombies," I thought. I straightened my headband and took off in a similar mode, but when I got about five yards down the runway, something within me rebelled. I let out a yelp, kicked off my high-heel shoes, and gave way to the rhythm.

Bouncing from one barefoot to the other in rhythm with the pow-wow music, lifting each foot high off the ground, mobilized the fringe into flight. I rocked from the waist forwards and backward and then added a pirouette. The long fringe whirled, taking on a life of its own. I couldn't help but throw in a shimmy for good measure. Teethed on cowboy and Indian films, I had seen zillions of pow-wows, and the energetic dancing and chanting were embedded into my genetic code. How was it possible to simply slink down the runway with that rousing rhythm?

As I worked my way back to the starting point, I began to reflect on what punishment I might receive. Would I have to sit in the corner, as I did at school, or would I be scalped without mercy? The music stopped, and I heard a noise. It sounded like applause. It was applause. Roberto shouted, "*Brava…..brava, perfetto!* Perfect! Never in my wildest dreams would I have imagined that would work, but it did." Roberto continued, "Alona is a Genius. She told me you wouldn't be the most polished, but you would add something unforgettable to the show. She was right!"

I thought to myself, and I'm not getting any credit for my dazzling performance? It's all about Alona's great intuition. Oh well, Alona can receive the recognition as long as I receive my money. I smiled and commented, "I'm so glad you liked it, Mr. Cavallini, the show needed some spicing up, and I was raised on Tabasco." The other girls were in a huddle planning a manifestation or perhaps a boycott. No, they were pleased I made a fool of myself, thus boosting their own egos. They congratulated me, and the spokeswoman said, "We were so glad to discover you weren't having a seizure or rabies fit. You did very well - you looked just like a Navajo Indian."

We had another dress rehearsal and then spent the rest of the day trying on all of Roberto's models to make sure the seamstresses didn't need to alter anything and to pinpoint who looked best in what. Roberto was pleased with himself – he was a perfectionist, and I could see he had a colossal career in front of him.

Three more days of shows and tediously trying on clothes, I was more than ready to get going to the fashion capital of the world, PARIS. Johanna and I would accompany Roberto in his jumbo jeep, while the other three girls would take a train.

I was privileged to share the back seat with a huge hind leg of dry-cured pork, better known as Prosciutto di Parma. Thinly sliced and served uncooked, it was a delicacy to be properly washed-down with a Reserve Red Wine – Barbera d'Alba. Roberto had cases of fine wine, tucked under all his designs, to be offered to his VIP clients who made orders or those who needed some coaxing.

He ordered an XL stand at the *Prêt à Porter* (Ready to Wear) fash-ion-fair to incorporate a social corner where he could invite his clients to his natal region's specialties. Hospitality is a dominant gene in the Italian temperament. It flows naturally like fine wine and is inviting, never con-trived or forced. Roberto had a relaxed, comfortable personality that enhanced his networking. He had the rare quality of being a creative art-ist who was dually apt in self-promotion and sales. He was naturally charming and drew people to himself, like a powerful magnet.

Roberto explained that the drive from Florence to Paris was an easy twelve hours, and we would start the following morning at 7 am. I had bought a bunch of bananas, some packs of peanuts, a few candy bars and a bottle of spring water, just in case I experienced a sugar-drop. Of course, I could munch on the leg of cured ham and varieties of pungent cheese that were my backseat companions.

We took off at 7 am on the dot, like gypsies loaded down with our life's belongings, off to graze in greener pastures. We zipped through the empty city that was slowly awakening like a hungry bear from hiberna-tion. There were churning growls from the dilapidated garbage trucks grinding up yesterday's fun and the sound of delivery trucks unloading supplies for today's toss of the dice. Within twenty minutes, we were roll-ing along the Tuscany countryside filled with cypress trees, olive groves, vineyards, and ancient hamlets. I thought out loud, "Can there be more to life than this?"

Reflecting on my quest to become a model in Paris, I could now see it unfolding through a series of coincidences. Or does my higher-power have a plan in all this? Time will tell. Meanwhile, I hoisted my hair up into a high pony-tail and reveled in the fact that everything seemed to be going my way, la-la-la. A few minutes elapsed, and then Roberto slipped a classical tape into his dashboard tape-deck. "Cool," I remarked. It wasn't often you saw that feature in European cars.

20. PARIS

We rolled into the big city at rush hour. You needed nerves of steel to drive in Paris – it was a modern form of jousting. However, Roberto was used to driving in Florence and Rome, so he used the same tactics, borrowing the sidewalks and neutral ground.

He announced, "I've chosen a hotel on Île Saint Louis – the heart of Paris and center of the medieval old city." The small island sat in the middle of the Seine River and connected to the larger island of Cité by the bridge, *Pont Saint Louis*. I was thrilled. We were bordering the avant-garde neighborhoods of Sant-Germain des Pres, Les Halles and the Latin Quarter. Notre-Dame was a stone's throw away. *La Rive Gauche* (the left bank of the Seine River) is known for jazz, the Latin Quarter, and a long and historic string of writers, artists, and philosophers. In fact, it's where they say that Paris "learned to think."

Roberto knew Paris inside and out. He was on the look-out for a good location for another boutique - after all, Paris was the global destination for up and coming fashion designers. It was their aspiration to be represented in this hallowed city. Roberto had a lot of get-up-and-go plus gumption.

As Roberto pulled up to a hotel that was previously a private mansion, Johanna and I jumped out with our bags, and we were told he'd be back to pick us up the following morning at 7:30 am. Roberto pulled away in his oversized-jeep, barely squeezing into the narrow, cobblestone street. He said he would sleep at a friend's place so he'd have a garage to lock up his ton of priceless goods.

We checked in, put our bags into our antique room, freshened up, and hit the streets again. Paris is an extraordinarily elegant city. Everything is displayed with meticulous, artistic perfection. We decided to have one course at the famous restaurant, *La Brasserie*. We were met with a frown – perhaps we looked like "one-course" girls. On the other hand, Parisians rated "10" in arrogance and downright rude behavior. It was almost comical how impolite they were - but I wasn't in the mood to laugh.

We were abruptly led to a table next to the gents' room. Johanna was a classical beauty clothed in understated good-taste, even though I wore faded jeans and a T-shirt. My "don't mess with me" flip side rose up and demanded. "Where is the manager of this joint?" I was ignored. I pranced back up to the entrance and found the *maître d'hôtel* (head waiter). I told him the restaurant was nearly empty and complained that we were seated next to the *stinky toilette*. The head waiter raised his eyebrows and said, "So what?" with a thick accent. I realized they wouldn't have cared if we were the Queen of Sheba and Cleopatra.

I told Johanna the head-honcho said we could sit anywhere we pleased. At least that's how I interpreted his reply. The restaurant was half empty since it was early, so we found a table where we could people-gaze. I made the decision, right then and there, that no Parisian was going to rain on my parade. If they were victims of a culturally negative attitude, I would not let it pierce my bubble. I refused to receive their attitude personally, and I would say a prayer for every insolent "frog" that crossed my path.

With a bit of persuasion, I talked Johanna into sharing a banana-split with me – the antidote for everything. The waiter was not euphoric when I requested one order with two spoons. Johanna reluctantly admitted, "*Sehr wunderbar*" (very wonderful.) I guess enough Americans dined there to justify adding that uncouth combo to their otherwise elegant French menu. We decided to call it a night and get to sleep early since we'd be helping Roberto set up the clothing stand in the wee hours of the following day.

Roberto picked us up at 7 am, and I jumped into the back seat with my friend porky. Roberto was always dressed in black and was wearing black designer jeans with a black T-shirt. When he dressed-up, he wore black jeans, a black silk shirt, a black sports jacket, and a black-tie. It may sound dismal, but on the contrary, it gave him a certain elegance and prestige. Like many Italian men of small stature, he felt confident surrounded by towering women.

There were display racks and everything else needed to organize the stand for a modest rental fee. After setting up the racks and social corner, we hauled in all of Roberto's sample models and hung them up. Then we lugged in sales-pitch-porky, the cases of wine, cheese and crackers. Phew, I only did one Lucille Ball-fall and was excused from some of the duties. Miss Know-it-All Germany was adept at constructing the racks and said I was a hindrance. She suggested I hang up the clothes and sit down.

I admit I was never great with Erector Sets or construction kits as a kid. What I lacked in common sense, I over-compensated with uncommon sense. At least it was more original, if not practical. The other three models arrived, cool as cucumbers, and apologized that they couldn't get to the exhibition hall earlier. Apart from trying on clothes for the customers, while Roberto wrote up the orders, we had scheduled runway shows in the afternoons. That's where I would shine.

Fashion week was a superb success, and our catwalk performances were in demand and always packed. Roberto was in his element – he had such a rocket response, he would have to hire more sewing ladies when he got back to Florence. It was personally good news because I was invited back for the next shows in six months. I agreed, and we shook hands. the deal was sealed. The honor code was good enough for me. I had no work permit in Europe, but I was permitted to work. So be it.

I had scaled the Eiffel Tower, inspected the Louvre and Museum de Orsay, viewed the statues of Rodin, and ruffled the feathers of the salesclerks in every boutique in Paris during my first visit more than a year and a half ago. My cousin Fran had completed her academic gymnastics, perfecting her French at the Paris-Sorbonne and returned to the States with her handsome Balkan boyfriend, so I was ready to hightail it back to Florence, then Rome and on to Ibiza.

We had a celebration meal together, and I couldn't resist a farewell song to Roberto. After half a glass of wine, I sang my adapted rendition of Frank's signature song, *"You Did it Your Way,"* using the pepper-mill as a mic. Roberto was bathed in applause by his fan-club of `models,' as well as the entire restaurant.

I awoke the following morning with a hangover – only half a glass of wine? Roberto was picking us up from our hotel in half an hour, so I splashed cold water in my face, brushed my teeth, jumped into my jeans and T-shirt, and Johanna and I were waiting downstairs at 7 am when Roberto drove by to collect us. I was glad to indulge in twelve lazy hours in the uncluttered rear seat of Roberto's jeep, listening to classical music. We were back in Roberto's palace in record time, then had a light dinner, and I plunged into a deep, delta sleep.

It was an incredible ten days – a goal attained and a dream realized, but I was still hungry. Something was missing in my diet of thrill-seeking. I would keep searching. . . .it was just around the corner. . . .that "something" that would fill the void that kept returning.

* * *

Meanwhile, I caught a taxi to the train station to head back to Rome. From there, I would collect my collage of worldly goods and head to Ibiza. That irresistible island, afloat in the Med, held some mystical answers. I was sure.

I was able to scribble into my journal the whirlwind events of the past ten days, but there was still plenty of space for the unknown. Flavio greeted me enthusiastically, *"Ciao Bella"* (Hello beautiful). I've been waiting in for you to arrive. You've had some urgent calls from Giovanni – he insists you call him the moment you arrive."

"Oh, I wonder what he wants. I'll just put my bag in my room, wash-up, and see what's so crucial."

Eventually, I called. "Hey Giovanni, Marie France here, how are you?"

"Finalmente sei tornato," "(Finally you're back), you need visas urgently for Tunisia, Algeria, Niger and Nigeria."

"Why?" I asked.

"So you can cross the Sahara, of course. We want to leave next week." Giovanni sounded frantic.

"No problem, I'm staying with Flavio, and his house is smack-dab in the middle of Embassy row. I'll start this afternoon."

Flavio overheard the conversation and announced he would come along with me to the Embassies. "There's only one way to cut through the bureaucracy, and that's with a friendly bribe," smirked Flavio. "Yikes, how much will that cost?" "Nothing for you; I'll get the Vice-Consulates free tickets to the opera, film openings or football games. So many people owe me a favor, I can collect this way." Flavio told me to wear something 'normal' and tie my hair back. I prayed for the impossible, four visas within a week. Flavio insisted I let him do the talking.

Like clockwork, we knocked out one embassy after the other. They all confirmed the visas would be ready within the week. All they had to do was put my request form on top instead of the bottom, where it belonged. It was no skin off their noses, and they'd have the best seat in the upcoming opera performance or football game.

I gave Flavio a bear hug and told him I wanted to invite him out to eat. "You can't afford to take me where I'd like to go. We'll eat at home. I have vegetables coming out of my ears from my organic patch in the garden. I'll whip up some *Carbonara al Roscioli* (Pasta with a creamy egg-based sauce dotted with pieces of succulent cured pork jowl)." "Great, I'll fix an American dessert and wash up." "*Cos' è un desert americano?*" "(What's an American dessert?)" "It's all healthy stuff – bananas, nuts and your homemade *gelato*. It's better known as a banana split."

WOW – CROSS the SAHARA DESERT! I can't believe such good fortune had fallen from the sky. It had to be from the God of the Universe. There must be some pieces of the puzzle there. I called Gio (my nickname for Giovanni) to tell him I'd have the four visas by Friday. "I hope so!" replied Gio anxiously. "The ticket for the ferry leaving mainland Italia to Sicily is this Sunday!"

"Gio, I'm saving my money to go back to India to invest in antique jewelry to sell in Europe. I don't have much extra cash to buy ferry tickets or supplies." "Not to worry. The main expense is diesel fuel, tons of spring water, and canned food. One person, more or less, doesn't matter; it's on me. My architect friend couldn't make it at the last minute, and I'd hate to drive for three weeks alone." Ah, that's what I wanted to hear - I'd be doing Gio a favor. *Olé*!

Gio and I met the next day at a café in Plaza del Popolo to discuss the voyage. I wore my Moroccan trousers and a hand-made turban to get into the mood. He explained that we would make the trip with two Land Rovers for safety and also for the company. His friend Marco would be going with his British girlfriend, Stella. Gio informed me that he would deliver the Land Rover he was driving to his friend Antonio, who owned a Safari Park in northern Nigeria. Marco would then drive Gio and me to Kano, Nigeria, where we would fly back to Rome.

"Whoa, too much information Gio, just tell me as we go along." Gio added, "Marco and I have been organizing and mapping out this desert-crossing for the past six months. It will be a rugged trip, but a trip you'll never forget." I laughed, "You don't have to sell me on this trip; I was sold when you first mentioned it in your country home, remember?"

Back at Flavio's, I set aside what I would take with me. I figured deserts were hot, so I planned on taking my three sarongs plus another three scarfs, a few T-shirts and my flip-flops. Flavio gasped, "*Mama Mia,* you need a jacket for the nights. Haven't you heard that deserts are freezing at night?" "No, we don't have deserts in Louisiana." "Here, if you want, take my old ski jacket." "Wow, perfect fit - *grazie,* Flavio."

I would have to put my return to Ibiza on hold because this was the trip of a lifetime. I would never be able to swing this kind of a crossing on my own. I felt it was destiny. Yes, my higher-power had this trip planned for me before the beginning of time. I was curious about what sort of earth-shattering events might take place. Meanwhile, I could also touch-up my fading suntan.

Just as they promised, the Vice Consulates came through with my visas in the nick of time, and Flavio handed them signed I.O.U.s for the tickets he had pledged them with his word of honor. Everyone was pleased with the deal, and I was satisfied with the "soft" corruption that kept Italy spinning. After all, it was Flavio's karma at stake.

The Big Day of departure arrived, and I was excited - those familiar butterflies that always fluttered when I was on the verge of a new exploit were flapping around wildly. I gave Flavio a hug and a double-cheek "air kiss," jumped into Gio's Land Rover, and we sped off to meet up with Marco and Stella... ... then southward-ho.

I couldn't help but ask Gio about the black Zodiac strapped to the roof of the jeep. It seemed unusual to haul an inflatable rubber boat to the desert. "*No, no è pieno d'acqua*" (No, no, it's filled with water), Gio explained that we needed enough water in case we got lost during a sand storm.

It seems he said that five Italians were found dead from dehydration last week in the Sahara Desert, and they were only six miles from the road. They were still seated in their Land Rover. I guess sand storms blow the dunes around, disorientating drivers. Gio's English wasn't great. Perhaps I misunderstood.

Having 20/20 vision, I spotted Marco and Stella from a distance - mainly because they had a Zodiac on top of their Land Rover also. On top of the Zodiac were strapped extra spare tires. We were the center of attention driving down to Sicily. I waved to people as we drove by since they were staring. I wish I'd have worn a pith helmet with a net veil to go with the `adventure-look.' I asked Gio if we should stop at a hardware store and buy some compasses. Gio laughed, "You have a great sense of humor." Perhaps he misunderstood me.

It was a five-hour journey from Rome to the tip of the boot of Italia. We then caught the car ferry from Calabria, and with the wind and waves, it felt like we were kicked over the Strait of Mesina to the shores of Sicily. The three and a half hour nauseous, nautical trip at least cut my appetite. I wondered if we'd be greeted by the mafia. We spent the night in Palermo, and I was looking around for machine-gun-toting-mobsters. It seemed very dull and quiet for all the hype surrounding the infamous city.

After exploring Palermo by car, we found a cozy restaurant that had a view onto their parking lot to keep an eye on the jeeps. The men ordered the food. They bragged that Sicilian food was some of the best in Italia, so we had to try the National Dish - Pasta with Sardines, fennel, and pine nuts. They also ordered *Caponata Aubergine* – no doubt named after the arch-villain of Chicago fame, Al Capone. Marco insisted on a big plate of raw red shrimp, another specialty of the island eaten with fresh strawberries.

I got to know Marco and Stella over dinner. Marco was about my height with an athletic build, even features, light-hearted personality, and spoke English. Stella was attractive, but nothing special, and spoke only Italian even though she was British. I read between the lines; she didn't like women. I ran into that quite often, but never mind. For the past five years, she lived in Italy and somehow snagged Marco, the co-heir to a media empire. His brother was the serious businessman of the two, so I was told.

We took the late-night ferry crossing the Strait of Sicily and arrived at Tunisia's capital eleven hours later. Gio and Marco slept in the jeeps to protect the three weeks of supplies needed for the perilous journey. Of course, I was unaware of any peril at any time.

Stella and I slept in berths that were reserved ahead of time. They were like berths on a train, with a curtain you could pull for privacy. Perfect, I did my breathing exercises; some low-volume chants, sang a Psalm quietly and slipped into a deep sleep. I dreamed I was leading a camel caravan over the dunes, and I had coded whistles to communicate with the rest of the caravan that trailed miles behind me. We were on our way to an Oasis when I woke up the next morning parched.

21. NORTH AFRICA – TUNISIA

We would soon arrive in North Africa and the quaint, coastal city of Tunis. I could see the town from a distance getting closer and anticipated the opportunity to surrender myself to the *Souk* (street market). We were the last to drive onto the ferry, thus first to roll off. Our guys were wise. A beach stretched out in front of the city like a welcome mat, beckoning us to enter.

We drove past a farmer plowing his field with a camel, then a shepherd walking along the road with his dusty sheep and a lady bouncing along on a donkey. My soul was drinking in the lovely, primitive lifestyle of yesteryear. Every structure in the city was whitewashed, reminding me of the town of Ibiza. The architectural style was the same since the North Africans ruled in Spain for seven hundred years. The island of Ibiza became the pit stop for the Carthaginians, from the ancient capital of Carthage and present-day Tunisia.

Marco volunteered to guard the Land Rovers while the three of us scattered around the market. I found a captivating little hole-in-the-wall with a ton of odds and ends. Hallelujah, I spotted an old, dirty glass jar filled with exquisite antique coral beads. I couldn't believe my eyes. They were the same beads I'd searched for in Kathmandu.

The source of the Tibetan coral was the Mediterranean. The precious old beads traveled along the silk trade route, finally ending up in the market of Lhasa, Tibet, in the 17th Century. I picked up the jar of ancient coral and said, "$10?" He countered my offer, "$15 last price." I agreed; it was a bargain. The beads were chunky, irregular shaped, dirty, with a crude hole for stringing them. I'm sure a Touareg Nomad from the Sahara Desert traded them for something practical, like a plastic bucket.

We took another drive around the city, viewing the mosques with lofty minarets and the back streets, with men sitting on the steps of their modest dwellings, weaving fine baskets with the lightning speed of magicians' hands. We then headed south. Our journey's first leg would be a nine-hour drive from Tunis to Tunisia's southern tip, near Algeria's border. Gio told me we would try to get to the border town of Douz, an oasis, plus the gateway to the Sahara Desert.

I was rarin' to go! CROSSING the SAHARA DESERT sounded so romantic, so inaccessible, so daunting, and definitely a topic to drop into future conversations. Gio explained that Sahara is the biggest hot desert in the world. It is the size of the United States, with only two and a half million inhabitants. "How interesting," I replied, as I struggled to hear him.

The Land Rover rattled so loudly that I had to concentrate on deciphering Gio's words through his ʻthick as molasses' accent and the squeaks of metal on metal. The vibration caused by speeding across the washboard corrugated sand hi-way muffled his voice.

However, the vibration was quite relaxing, like those massage chairs you see at shopping centers that you get ʻall shook up' for a mere quarter. By now, all recognizable semblance of a road had disappeared, but there was a large white painted rock every mile or so to guide us southward. I was warned that the average daytime temperature was around 100° F but could easily zoom up to 120° F. However, without the Louisiana humidity, I knew I could manage.

The sharp, arid environment had knocked all the curl and frizz out of my hair, so it was easy to wrap my long straight locks around my head, snuggly held with bobby pins. I then made a turban from one of my scarves. It looked ʻcool' and prevented the nano-dust from the desert to work its way to my scalp and into my ears. Most importantly, it prevented the scorching sun from prematurely aging my skin, especially when we'd stop for a break and wandered around the dunes.

I soon realized why the nomads wore turbans and pulled a veil across their nose and mouth. If not, you breathed in a gallon of dust or swallowed it. I wish I had thought of bringing a chapstick.

My three travel companions made fun of my turban and called me King Tut until they succumbed to the mummy-wrap also. We saw nomads on camels in the distant dunes, and Gio felt the need to inform me that Dromedary Camels had been domesticated for thousands of years and long used by the nomads to haul gold and salt. He said they had large, thick lips so they could feed on thorny plants, slits for nostrils, and heavy eyebrows and lashes to protect themselves from punishing sandstorms. The fat-filled hump on their backs enabled them to travel without food or water for days and when they arrived at an oasis, they could consume more than thirty gallons of water in a matter of minutes.

Gio seemed to have a desert-camel fetish; he even smoked Camel cigarettes. Perhaps he wasn't allowed a sandbox as a kid or a camel either. However, it was fortunate that he wasn't the type who wanted to snorkel in the Caribbean.

Ever since I had first viewed "Lawrence of Arabia," I have dreamed of adventures in the desert. However, now it seemed more of a place to meditate and ponder where my life was heading. Walking around the dunes reminded me how everything returns to dust in the end and just how essential it is to celebrate the brief moments of life we have – or is there life on the other side of death? Something to ponder. . . . .

The further south we traveled, the more interesting the scenery became. The remarkable ripples of sand, rock-sculptures, and grassy shrubs took on new forms every few miles. It was like turning a kaleidoscope and getting a new and different view using the same elements. We passed a few ancient ruins and oasis villages. We then stopped for a supply of oasis palm fruit, being sold on the side of our sand-packed hi-way. The dates were naturally sweet, not encapsulated in a cocoon of sticky sugar, like the variety back home.

After nearly eight hours of shake-rattle-and-rolling along our route, the guys decided it would be more mystical to sleep near the Oasis of

Blidet, just nineteen miles short of Douz. It was almost sunset when we made camp. Gio pulled out the army cots and handed me a light-weight arctic sleeping bag. I placed it neatly on my cot and was glad I'd be a few feet above the creepy-crawlers of the night. Stella arrogantly made the fire and boiled water for the spaghetti. There were hundreds of cans of Bolognese, Carbonara, and pesto sauce, plus large chunks of parmesan cheese to grate on top.

The temperature was dropping, and my spirits were rising. 45°F felt good in my arctic bag with my warm turban pulled over my ears. There was such an awe-inspiring peace. After a few hours of Italian chatter and laughter, everyone settled down with a gas lantern to read. There was only the sound of pages turning or an occasional sigh. Peace, glorious peace! I had two books and a week old Herald Tribune. I read a chapter of my book, "The Power of Positive Thinking," and then started reading my Gideon guide. I wanted to sing some Psalms but read them instead. Within half an hour, we turned off our lanterns one-by-one, and the magic began.

There was a celestial majesty of sparkling lights spread overhead – without a beginning or an end. The arid, still atmosphere distorted the illusion of space. I stretched my hand towards the heavens, believing I could touch a star. I was alone with the Milky Way, and the stars seemed to anchor my existence and provide a measure of time and space. I felt an overwhelming connection to the stars as if I were part of them. I felt one-ness with the universe and its Creator for the first time in my life. I drifted off to sleep, knowing I belonged and that I was loved. It was a knowing that bypassed human thought or emotion, but I knew it was so.

We awoke as the sun snuck up from the horizon, without warning, filling the dawn with full daylight. Marco boiled some water for coffee with a buddy burner, and we ate digestive cookies with dates and nuts. Our next destination was the Oasis of Djanet. We were near Algeria's northern border and would need at least four days to reach Djanet. I read that Algeria was 90% desert, and we would cover a big chunk of it.

22. ALGERIA – SAHARA DESERT

It was day three when we encountered our first sand storm. By 11 am the strong wind whipped up into a fierce wind, then a blinding wind. We could see an impenetrable beige wall approaching us – then it slammed into us front-on from the south. The wall extended from the horizon into infinity, cutting all visibility. We were fully engulfed in the raging storm. Gio and Marco stopped the Land Rovers, and we remained safely inside, but the grit sifted through every crevice of the jeep. However, the sound of sand pelting metal took on a reassuring melody. I wound double layers of scarves over my face, but I was sure that all would be well despite the drama.

Our two boy-scouts had done their homework. We had two Zodiacs, still filled with water and tons of canned food. We had sophisticated compasses with us, and Marco, a seasoned sailor, could navigate by the stars. All was well, we thought.

We patiently waited out the violent storm. With the windows closed, the temperature skyrocketed at least fifteen degrees, but we had bottles of water to remain hydrated. It took about three hours for the storm to subside, and we were finally able to get out and look around. We felt like the first astronauts, stepping out onto the moon, not knowing what to expect. The dunes had shifted, and the corrugated sand road was not in sight. Marco said bravely, "No problem, a few more hours of wind will blow the loose sand off of the hard-packed road."

He was right; the corrugated ridges became visible once again. But, we couldn't get out of a patch of soft sand. The wheels of our jeep kept spinning and digging us deeper into the loose sand. Our four-wheel-drive was activated, but we remained immobilized. Marco said, "No problem, I have a shovel to remove the loose sand, plus I brought traction mats along with me." I got out of the car to see if I could help. Marco put the mats under the rear wheels. Gio advanced a few feet, then Marco screamed, *"Fermare"* (Stop). Gio advanced a few feet more, then Marco fed the mats back under the wheels. Four more maneuvers and we were on packed sand. Marco was our biggest asset, along with the Zodiac filled with water.

Fortunately, a white stone marker was visible in the distance, so it had not been obliterated by a wind-swept sand dune. While we were sitting in the car during the sand storm, I could hear the wind whooshing with the sound. . . ."Ye. . . .SHUA". . . ."YE. . . .SHUA." I felt I was cupped in the hands of The Almighty, and I prayed. It also revealed to me where my allegiance resided during this emergency.

My higher power had revealed Yeshua to me in the Giza Pyramid and then again on the hill of Golgotha in that church in Jerusalem, and now during the sandstorm. Back in Goa, Luke assured me that I would find what I was looking for if I continued to seek. How many more confirmations would I need before I was satisfied? I wanted to remain compassionate, all-encompassing, and tolerant, but I wondered if I became TOO open-minded, my brains would fall out. I would give that some thought later.

I looked forward to the evenings, the connectedness I felt while gazing into the galaxies, the oneness with the universe I experienced. I felt the heavens lean down and draw me near. I was a thrill-seeker, but I longed for my default emotion to be peace, the same desert peace I felt every evening under the stars.

The next evening we would roll into the Oasis Djanet, and there would be a small variety of simple hotels and local food. The idea of a lukewarm shower, a mattress, and some local food was inviting, but I'd miss my starry fix. Djanet was a large city for the desert, with a population of about 5,000.

As we drew closer, jagged rock formations came into view, and a vast grove of palm trees sprung up before we entered the city. The dwellings were cubes, connected with more cubes. The bricks were made from the local orange earth, some whitewashed with blue trim. Only tiny windows were visible, to keep invaders from penetrating as well as the harsh rays of the sun. The city was built on a hill, and the most affluent had the steepest walk to the top. The inhabitants were Tuareg Nomads. Who else would live in such a remote, god-forsaken paradise?

For the past three days, we'd only passed two trucks and no other foreign travelers. Due to the previous French colonization, many of the Tuaregs spoke colloquially adopted French. Most Italians chose French as a second language, so Gio and Marco were fluent and did well in finding the best, humble hotel. It also included a restaurant, so we ate there. I had my own mini room with a bathroom down the hall. What luxury! I stood my ground under the low-pressure shower while someone tried to knock the door down. In my best French, I shouted, *"Un moment."*

We all had couscous for supper - that was all they had. It was magnificent! The semolina was steamed on top of a mix of spiced mutton and vegetables. It was an edible work of art. The oasis was fertile enough to grow carrots, sweet potatoes, turnips, pumpkin, cabbage, and cilantro. Ground ginger, turmeric, and saffron were trucked in from Algiers.

Only one bite of couscous provoked a *déjà vu* and hurled me back to Morocco. That North African country was my introduction to Africa more than a year ago, and a significant catalyst to my future travels. My ex-roommates from New Orleans were tucked away in the coastal village of Pont Blondin. David attended an elite Swiss hotel school and excelled in all but the French language. He miraculously convinced his father into financing a year's sabbatical in Morocco, with his girlfriend Joey, so that he could brush up on that agonizing language.

Brushing up on French in Morocco was like brushing up on English in the swamps of Louisiana. David and Joey spent their days creating ex-

travagant Moroccan dishes to break the monotony of their French lessons. Gastronomy was their passion and their gift. It was there I sampled
their mouth-watering couscous, and tonight's supper in Algeria was nearly
as good.

Joey insisted we try the Public Hammam (Turkish bath). We were
swept away with the idea of an exotic steam bath and massage in the spa.
The reception area was desolate. We caught sight of cubby holes with
clothes hanging out, so we stuffed ours in also. We then crept down the
dark, cavernous hallway from one scalding torture chamber to the next,
which led us into a large medieval dungeon filled with so much steam it
was hard to breathe. We were stark naked when confronted by robust
sweaty ladies lounging around in their underwear. Rather than turn back,
we sat down on a cement block and imitated the natives.

They had buckets of steamy water and pumice stones. An over-
zealous local lady picked up my limp arm then started scrubbing down
my entire body. With despair, I watched my costly suntan hit the floor
and swiftly disappear down the drain. We then took the orange peel and
bark floating in another bucket, rubbed the peel over our skinless bodies,
and scraped our teeth with bark. One snickering nomad explained that
was the trash bucket, and the peels were from their citrus snack, and the
bark had already been used. I finally gasped, "Joey, I've gotta' get out of
here! The heat and stench are overwhelming."

We were later told that the Hammam was the public bathhouse for
female nomads who wandered in for their yearly bath and scrub-down. It
took a month and ten shampoos to extract the `natural' perfume of those
desert women from my ton of thick hair.

* * *

I returned my thoughts to our exquisite couscous in Oasis Djanet, where
I was mocked for eating almost half the huge platter. I was still a bottom-

less pit and hard to fill up. We were then served hot, sweet mint tea, a good exclamation mark to a perfect meal.

The Tuareg Nomads were tall and slim with relatively fair skin. Many were shepherds and also had goat's milk on tap to make cheese and yogurt. Their flocks of goat, sheep, cattle, and camels often ended up in a pot to keep the tribes' hunger at bay and breed healthy offspring to carry on the taxing nomad life.

We waddled away to our rooms and took off early the next morning to visit the ancient caves with prehistoric drawings and fairy-tale orange rock formations. The town of Djanet and the surrounding area stand out in my mind for its brute, dramatic beauty. As we drove south, the sculptured rock formations became more impressive, and the bright orange color of the stone and sand gave it a surrealistic aura. We spent most of the day wandering around in a blissful daze, intoxicated by such spectacular beauty.

Our next destination was Tamanrasset. Gio told me it would take about twenty hours of driving, broken up into four or five days, depending on how often we stopped. It was during our second evening, with the usual pattern of a peaceful supper followed by reading, that my world turned upside down.

After another magnificently scenic day, we had a light but filling pasta dish. As I was squatting down to pick up the kettle of boiling water to pour over the mint leaves, I felt a sharp pain piercing my right leg. I knew it was the safety pin holding my sarong together that must have opened and jabbed that tender spot with a vengeance. It took all the self-control I could muster not to throw the boiling kettle into the air and scream. I remained composed, set the kettle down again, and stood up. At that moment, something fell to the ground. I took the lantern to inspect what it was. Gio bent over with me and audibly inhaled, "A death-stalker scorpion! I have only seen photos of that type of scorpion in books."

Gio mimicked John Wayne, and cooly opened his pocket knife and poured some whiskey on the blade. He then sliced into the puncture marks the scorpion had engraved on my leg, sucked out the venom, and spit it into the sand. Stella said smugly; "Anyway, scorpions die after they sting someone." That information didn't help my situation or promote solace. Strangely enough, I felt relatively peaceful, but I could see the terror in my travel companions' eyes. I could read their minds: "This hippie's demise will put a huge dent in our travel plans. What will we do with the body? Bury it in the sand and burn the hippie's passport? Drive to the next village, two days away, and report it to the nomad police?"

I tried to comfort my traveling party. "I grew up in Louisiana, and when our dogs got bitten by a snake, they'd blow up for a day or so, then the swelling would go down, and they'd build up immunity." Marco volunteered, "My grandmother told us to put a freshly cut onion on any type of bite, and it would draw out the venom and act as an anti-inflammatory." I added, "Great idea, that should do the trick." Stella complained that we only had one onion left. Meanwhile, I retreated to my army cot and held the half-onion over my wound, like a good soldier.

Everyone pretended all was A-OK and began to read as usual. However, I could see their three pairs of eyes glancing at me over the tops of their books. I was tempted to gasp loudly, double over dramatically, then fall off my cot, roll over in the sand and let my tongue hang out. I remembered a scene like that from the Audie Murphy war film, "To Hell and Back." But I didn't want to take a chance of shocking our drivers too badly and disabling them from driving us out of this desert.

I was surprised by the peace I experienced; there was no decision to make. There was no doctor to call or hospital to rush to or antidote to take, so I just read my little Gideon book. It crossed my mind whether I should write a "farewell" letter to my family, just to let them know I was having the time of my life when the incident took place. But I drifted off into REM sleep.

I awoke with a huge swollen area that extended down my right leg, but I was alive. My leg became the focus of attention. Every few hours, everyone wanted to inspect "the spot." I thought I needed some sympathy, so I dragged my leg, alternating with a few little hops, like Rico "Ratso" Rizzo in the Midnight Cowboy. That didn't work, so I copied the lumbering foot-dragging monster that Boris Karloff portrayed in "The Mummy." It worked - I was excused from helping with supper. It took a few days before I was as good as new. We were all given instructions to shake out our clothes before putting them on and to look where we were stepping.

We had a breathtaking drive to Tamanrasset and stocked up on onions and other vegetables and fruits. This oasis town was highly populated, considering its location. It had a river running nearby, with the same name. We found a great spot outside of the city to plunge off a rock into a deep pool carved out of the rocks. It was mega-refreshing after a hot, sandy day, and we didn't have to go into a hotel for a shower. But needless to say, our guys asked around for the best restaurant in town. We feasted on chicken *tagine. Tagine* is the conically shaped terracotta vessel the ingredients are cooked in. Along with the chicken and vegetables, *ras el hanout,* a mix of exotic spices, enhanced the extraordinary flavor.

I'd always get dressed up to eat out. My three sarongs were rotated daily, as were my T-shirts and scarves. On our nights out, I added my silver cobra belt and the coral necklace I had strung together from the chunky beads I found in Tunis. To top it off, I wore a fashion-wrapped turban.

The trip south to Agadez would take several days, but passing the border into Niger was only eight hours away. This Sahara/sub-Sahara nation was one of the least traveled countries in the world. We met not one tourist on our voyage and celebrated our good fortune. We went through the borders like diplomats due to the special passes Gio obtained. Even though it was a rugged trip, I would be sorry when it ended.

23. NIGER – SAHARA DESERT

Niger, although rich in uranium, is one of the poorest countries in Africa. The nation's economy centers on subsistence livestock and meager crops - few formal jobs exist. Since their independence from France in 1960, there has been a haphazard and austere military rule.

With this backdrop, we drove into Agadez, welcomed by smiling faces from the tall, proud, handsome inhabitants. The women were my height, with bolt-upright postures, from years of balancing water atop their heads - often transporting the liquid gold for miles. Their skin was a beautiful shade of ebony and their teeth, in contrast, were sparkling white like an advertisement for Colgate.

The market place was vast and colorful with laughing, hopeful merchants. A hundred vendors laid out their items on woven mats while goats, donkeys, and albino camels wandered around aimlessly. Women wore brightly colored dresses, most often "fire-engine red." Huge silver hoop earrings graced their ears. I felt like an odd-ball and wanted to imitate their beauty and style. There wasn't the overt poverty I witnessed on the streets of Bombay. It appeared to be a happy-go-lucky mud-brick town in the middle of the dusty, windy Sahara. I was curious to know what adventure this landlocked dust bowl could possibly hold.

Gio located the best restaurant in town. It was near the Grand Mosque and included a parking lot where we could survey the jeeps. We all voted to sleep outside the noisy city. Seems the national dish, *Djerma* was not on par with couscous, but a close second. The stew was filled with lots of oasis vegetables, scrawny chicken bits, curry powder, and a strange but familiar flavor. Peanut butter! Peanuts have more protein per ounce than beef steak - perhaps that was the secret of the locals' impressive stature. To top off the weird but exciting meal, we had fried bananas for dessert. I dreamed about a banana split with chocolate sauce but was warned against ice cream in Africa. I heard it could be as venomous as the scorpions, so I stayed clear.

More important than just having a good meal, our guys swung a deal with the town elder and herdsman, Beluchi, to guide us to a dinosaur graveyard the following morning. I wondered if it was a scam. No, the people were too simple and sincere for that. DINOSAUR treasure hunt! Could it be true?

Come to find out, Marco was a closet case paleontologist. I guess he was too sportive and `cool' to admit to his friends that his secret passion was paleontology. He knew everything there was to know about dinosaurs, from their diet to their poop. The desert of Niger was well known amongst those in the know, that it held an immense quantity of unexcavated dinosaur skeletons.

The drawback for the nation of Niger was their lack of money and know-how to carry out the delicate work of excavation and reconstruction of the ancient bones. But, it opened up semi-illegal jobs for local guides such as our Beluchi. He explained that his name translated into "provided God approves," so we felt safe on this secret mission of bone-scouting.

My knowledge of dinosaurs was gleaned from a series of impacting films throughout my youth. As kids, my brother and I were often parked in the local movie theater with double features when my mother needed some "space" from our endless squabbles. You only needed a box top from Blue Plate Margarine and a dime to buy a ticket for the afternoon matinee.

The first dinosaur I remember was a clumsy T-Rex conquered by King Kong. More recently, there was the remake of "One Million Years B.C." in 1966, starring a Ceratosaurus and the horned Triceratops that stole the limelight from Raquel Welch.

Marco explained, "We will be looking for Nigersaurus in the Gadoufaoua strata formed during the early to middle Cretaceous periods, 145-105 million years ago. They grew to about thirty feet and were unique with their delicate skulls, long necks, and extremely wide mouths, lined with up to five-hundred teeth, adapted for eating plants close to the earth."

Marco added, "It is presumed that over two million years ago there was only one big 'supercontinent' called Pangea, and dinosaurs roamed the entire connected earth. Nigersaurus were herbivores, signifying this no-man's-land was once rich with forests and streams." The regional dinosaur sounded like the description of Fred and Wilma's pet "Dino" of Flintstone fame, with a mouth shaped like a vacuum cleaner.

I was pumped and ready for the treasure hunt. I wore a sarong-type skirt with an open slit over one leg so I could skip or run, plus a long-sleeved T-shirt and a high turban for extra protection from the blazing sun. Our guide explained to us that when a dinosaur bone surfaced the sand, it could be identified by its light blue hue. The blue tinge was caused by the stark contrast of the bone against the beige sand. Beluchi was nearly blind but said he could sense where the graveyard was. He would point from the front seat of the jeep, and Gio would follow. I sat in the back seat while Marco & Stella followed in their Land Rover. Beluchi then announced, "*Arrêtez!*" (Stop!) Gio slammed on the breaks so hard; I almost ended up in the front seat on our guide's lap.

Since the desert was completely flat in that area, Marco suggested we would cover more area if we all walked in different directions. If anyone spotted a bone, they'd whistle for the others. He told us to walk in a zig-zag fashion to cover more territory. Marco also explained that if we touched our tongue to a fossil, it would stick if it was osseous matter - due to the porous, spongy nature of bone. I had no qualms about licking a dinosaur bone and looked forward to it.

Having cultivated a good shrill whistle over the years, I could be heard in Timbuktu. I slung a cloth bag over my shoulder to carry a bottle of water, dates and nuts, then rambled off south-bound. After about twenty minutes of staring at every inch of sand within range, I understood, firsthand, the meaning of a mirage. It seems when the intense desert sun heats the sand, which in turn heats the air, it bends light rays and reflects the sky. It appeared that there was a pool of water just ahead, where I could have a refreshing swim, but it kept evaporating as I neared. "Whoa!"

I hummed the desert song about a horse with no name as I scanned left to right and back again with undivided attention. After about fifteen minutes, I saw a blue-tinged mass protruding from the sand. It was about fifteen yards away. I started to fast-walk, then jog towards it. I stood over the bone with my heart racing, then got down on all fours and had a good lick! EUREKA! The bone tingled my tongue, then stuck to it for a few seconds. I jumped up and started whistling. Gio waved his hat, and Marco waved his shirt to signify their recognition of my whistle and briskly walked to where I staked my ground, my claim!

Marco had a brush with him and started whisking away the loose sand. The mass resembled a gigantic vertebra, so the three of us began brushing with our hands. We uncovered about eight feet of connecting vertebrae on one side of the exposed bone and then another fourteen feet in length on the other side. Marco's dream had come true, except he was crushed to find the fragile skull of the Nigersaurus fragmented into about twelve pieces.

It was illegal to do what we were doing. There were huge fines for stealing fossils and perhaps for photographing them. Marco couldn't resist – he took one photo of the ancient spine and tail bones, plus another of the skull fragments. He vowed he'd be back with permits and a team of professionals.

The main thing was, his hunch was confirmed, and we walked back to the jeeps with our heads held high. The noonday sun rays were too strong – we sought the shelter of the vehicles. Beluchi was patiently waiting – waiting was his new profession. The guys gave him a generous tip on top of the agreed fee, and we brought him back to Agadez.

Gio had an architectural project starting within a week and needed to get back to Rome, so we left the next morning to deliver our Land Rover to Gio's friend Antonio with the safari park. We'd fly back from Kano, the second-largest industrial city of Nigeria. It was only about twelve hours to Kano – two or three days driving, including a visit with Gio's friend.

We left early the next morning, and I started to feel wistful about leaving the unique, starry heavens of the desert and the oneness I experienced nightly with my Creator.

We drove until dusk and made camp just before nightfall. We had to go slower than usual due to the pot-holes. We lit our lanterns for a nightly read when Gio pointed out lights in the distance. It looked like a small village or gathering – perhaps a group of nomads working their way across the desert with bags of salt…..or gold. Marco suggested we walk over there and check it out. We had been in the car all day, so it would be good to oxygenate our blood.

* * *

The landscape was totally flat, so we would easily find the way back to our camp with the light from our gas lanterns. After about ten minutes, we heard drums beating, and as we neared the gathering, we could single out the typical sound of the kora, an instrument with twenty-one strings, played by plucking. The closer we got, the louder the drums boomed.

Wow, I felt the vibration, "There's a party going on…..awesome!" I felt like dancing. We arrived at the merry-making, which was lit up by torches. There were entire families, not only the usual all-men caravans. We were met with euphoric, grinning faces. The gathering should have been up-in-arms and shocked to have four uninvited foreigners wander into their celebration. However, they seemed ecstatic. I wondered if they were drugged.

I mimed the ladies' moves to perfection; I felt like I had been dancing with them since ever. There was a bond in rhythm and mood. My three companions joined in with stiff, awkward moves but seemed to enjoy being part of the happening. No one spoke French, so the guys couldn't ask them the reason for their revelry. Perhaps this was a nightly event.

After about twenty minutes, a dancing lady handed me a baton, led me by the hand up onto a platform, and demonstrated how I should wave the wand. I got the hang of it immediately and felt like the head majorette at a half-time football show. I was honored to lead the festival and was amazed at the following gathered at the base of my pedestal. Were we perhaps the first white people they'd ever seen, and they thought we had fallen from the cosmos? I wonder if they thought I was a goddess that demanded adulation?

Regrettably, after a short while, the mood changed. It became somewhat frenzied, and the ravers looked entranced. A teenage girl started to pull on my hair, and there was an atmosphere of confusion and even mayhem. Gio shouted, "When I count to three, make a run for it, and don't look back."

I had the disadvantage of being perched on a rickety stage – I jumped down but tripped on a loose plank and ending up spread-eagle below. I spit the sand out of my mouth, stood up, and passed the baton on to a frowning female. Then, I hi-tailed it towards the lights of our camp.

I was afraid to look back if thirty people were on my heels, but I followed instructions and focused on the jeeps. We were in a vulnerable position - thirty against four, in the middle of the desert in Niger, a day away from the nearest town. I prayed a quick, meaningful prayer, "HELP!" I believed in miracles and discovered I could run as fast as the men and caught up with them in seconds. Stella dropped out of sight. I thought, just as well, she'll make a good peace offering. Perhaps they'll back off after capturing her.

We arrived back to camp where Gio and Marco had heavy iron wrenches and some knives. We were panting but relieved to reach safety. Stella came straggling in five minutes later and shot us a look of daggers. I repented for my unkind thoughts. No one was behind her, PHEW! But we decided to move camp anyway so we could sleep peacefully. A lesson was learned – do not gatecrash desert nomad parties!

We started early to have a few hours at the safari park with Gio's friend Antonio. We were making good time when our Land Rover suddenly dropped slightly on the right side where I was sitting. I looked up and saw our right front wheel rolling in front of us at record speed. There were also sparks of fire ricocheting off the rim that was heating up in the sand. Gio remarked calmly, "Oh, the bolts must have been rattled loose with the corrugated roads." It would have been comical if it had happened to someone else. Marco was ahead of us, so Gio blasted the horn non-stop. We needed the help of muscular Marco.

Marco made a U-turn and rolled the tire back to us, laughing. The guys fixed it within half an hour, and we were back on the sand-packed, wash-board road again. I belted out Willy Nelson's hit tune, "On the Road Again," and realized how good it was to have capable guys around....... sometimes.

Another five hours, and we'd be delivering our Land Rover to Gio's friend at the Safari Park. We'd spend the night there, and then Marco would drive us to Kano, where we'd catch a flight back to Rome. At least that was the plan.

24. NIGERIA

We arrived at the border of Nigeria, and Gio handed the customs officer our special passes, which turned out to be MONEY. I saw a bill sticking out of the folded paper and cringed, hoping we wouldn't get arrested for bribery. The guy ordered us out of the jeeps, and Gio handed the guy a bigger bill. Yikes, now we were in for it. The officer told us we could get back into our vehicles and waved us on. We had our visas in order, our passports up-to-date, and we weren't smuggling anything that I knew about. Gio explained that a tip was expected, and it saved three hours of having his vehicle ransacked. "Besides, border customs officers have low wages, it's expected." "Oh, okay, if you say so." We sped south.

By now, it was getting a bit greener, with more shrubs and the occasional tree. The further south we drove, the greener it got. Another few hours and we turned off the main road south to get to the safari park where we would leave our Land Rover with Gio's good friend Antonio. It was heartwarming to see Italian reunions, especially among men. Those sincere, unabashed man hugs don't exist with other nationalities – at least not to that extent. A handshake is the most intimate contact most men have in northern Europe and the States.

The three guys laughed so hard they were out of breath. Antonio caught up with news of their mutual friends in Rome, The Eternal City. By now, I understood Italian quite well but speaking that melodious language was a real challenge. I felt lost if I couldn't interject humor or cryptic comebacks, the real me.

I could understand Antonio's business was doing well, and he had some key contracts with agencies that kept his rustic cabins filled up for the high season. Antonio's English was excellent - since he had lots of Brits, Germans, Dutch, and Scandinavians as customers. I shared some of the humorous highlights of our trip through Africa, and Antonio roared with laughter. I only spiced it up slightly.

We had a typical four-hour meal with multiple courses and lots of dialogue - some sarcasm, but mostly light with hilarity. However, Antonio spoke earnestly about the nightmare of deforestation in northern Nigeria. He explained that with erosion and drought, the desert would engulf his safari park within fifty years. Already the locals' drop in crop production was dramatic. He spoke about moving further south.

It was low season, so I was allotted a small cabin and looked forward to a soak and a real mattress. My sleeping bag cushioned the army cot but was no substitute for a bona fide bouncy mattress. I retired early to try and coax my body back into shape to return to civilization – if Rome qualified as being called civilized.

Marco and sulky Stella drove us to Kano and let us off at the downtown Union Bank. Marco got out of his Land Rover and gave me a heartfelt hug, and gave his good friend Gio a genuine man-embrace. Stella waved from the window, and I wished them a safe trip to Kenya and across the Indian Ocean.

Gio had to wait half an hour to be attended to in that shabby bank. He returned, looking miffed and explained, "There's a strike going on in Italy and I can't get a transfer from any of my accounts. I only have enough money for one flight. So I'll take it and send your ticket to Nigerian Airways as soon as I get back.

Wow, that sounded awesome. I'd have time to check out the local market and get to know Kano. "Yea, that sounds good, Gio," I replied. He said, "Here, take my Nikon camera, and if by any chance the ticket doesn't arrive, just sell my camera, it's worth a lot more." "OK, good of you, Gio, but I'm sure the ticket will arrive." I told Gio, "Hey, don't worry,

I'll find a cheap hotel and check with the airline every day." English was the official language in Nigeria, so I knew I could find my way around without a hitch.

I gave Gio a huge hug and said with sincerity, "Thanks for the trip of a lifetime! See you in Rome in several days." I felt terrible for Gio, I knew he was embarrassed by the situation, but I comforted him. Of course, I had my folks' Gold American Express card tucked safely in my body pouch, as well as some traveler's checks. I wouldn't need to sell his Nikon, but it was handy to have, just in case. All would be well. I flagged a taxi and asked for a cheap hostel near a five-star hotel. It would be vital to have a swimming pool nearby and air-conditioning during the hottest hours of the day.

My little hostel was the equivalent of one dollar a day but felt like a fifty cents a day dive. I'd soak up the air conditioning from the Palace Hotel down the block, swim, then duck into my dive for the night. I discovered the only way to sleep was when I was evaporating, so every twenty minutes, I'd stand under the shower and then jump into bed with the fan directed on me point-blank. But never mind, I looked forward to the local market.

The market was only a few miles away, so I taxied there bright and early the next morning. There were a bunch of eager young boys waiting in front of the entrance, so I applied my time-proven tactic by picking the strongest looking kid and announced, "This is my guide while I'm here." Oruko was cheerful and spoke English impeccably. He was excited to show me around the market. We started with goatskin bags. I was on the lookout for things to sell Mama Loula back in Rome. The market was vast, and it took us three hours to walk up and down all the aisles. I bought a few odds and ends but would return the next day for more. I gave Oruko a good tip and told him I'd be back the following morning at 9 am.

I couldn't wait to get to the Palace Hotel for a swim and some A/C. Nigeria Airways was within walking distance, so I'd wait until the next day to check for my flight ticket. The lounge area at the Palace was great, even free peanuts on the tables. I brought my journal with me to jot down my past weeks' desert adventures. As I wrote, a deep sadness overcame me. I would miss the cold, clear, desert nights with the canopy of twinkling stars overhead. But, most of all, I would miss that feeling of oneness with the universe and the creator of it all, my Creator.

As Marco was a patient teacher, my knowledge of the stars increased tenfold. I absorbed a lot from his constellation lectures. The brightest planets were Venus, Mars, Mercury, Saturn, and Jupiter. Even though they were visible every night, it was rare that all five could be seen simultaneously. I could pick them out of the Milky Way. Marco tried to equip us nightly for celestial navigation by studying the position of the stars. Ursa Major, the Great Bear; Orion, the Hunter; Taurus, the Bull; Gemini, the Twins and Ursa Minor, the Little Bear, had all become my intimate friends. I smiled and thanked my lucky stars for the awesome opportunity of having danced with the universe.

* * *

There was a poster advertising a well-known group from Nigeria who had borrowed the style and the tunes of Bob Marley. They would be performing here in the Palace Hotel tomorrow night. Hot-diggity-dog! I felt like some reggae since it was becoming the rage. I noticed quite a few vendors at the market had dreadlocks. I'd get myself all decked out, and with the humidity, my hair would frizz nicely. I'd have the longest afro in the club. I decided not to check for my flight ticket until after tomorrow. I needed just a bit more time in Kano.

While evaporating, I had solid, short intervals of sleep and was ready to attack the market. Oruko was there waiting for me and waved as the taxi pulled up. He announced, "This lady is mine, tell ʿem." I told the bunch of boys that Oruko was my boy. We strutted off together towards the jewelry stands and artisan leather collections. I invited Oruko for lunch and discovered he could eat up a storm. We feasted on *EwaAgoyin*, which was a spicy bean stew served with Agege Bread. We then munched some corn on the cob, topped off with bananas grilled on embers - delicious and even nutritious!

After about three hours, I taxied back to my hostel with my stash of stuff to resell in Rome. I then high-tailed it over to the Palace Hotel with my change of clothes and enjoyed a relaxed afternoon at the pool, had a power-shower, and slipped into my snazzy striped crop top and hip hugger jeans. I was ready to dance my blues away. The reggae group, "Rock-Out," started at 9 pm, so I filled up on the courtesy peanuts. The hotel club was packed since the well-known group drew lots of locals.

Whoa, what a rhythm, I started to dance by myself. You had to catch the rhythm of the music and then rock with it – moving your shoulders right to left, right to left. Then extend your arms while leaning back, first in a circular motion, then a cross-the-heart motion, and finally bringing your arms back over your head while remaining in the rhythm. Precisely the same motions I'd learned in London, the moves were international.

I soon had a dreadlocked partner who said, "Cool, you really rock." My forte was that I was a formidable mimic. I just copied his every move. I soon discovered we were alone on the dance floor, and a crowd encircled us, clapping and swaying. I later learned my partner was the ʿKano King of Reggae,' and I was accepted as a sister. With the help of the humidity, I had the frizziest long afro in the club. My toasted-tan from the Sahara also helped.

Everyone called me "sister" and insisted on "high-five" acceptance. After a few hours of dancing non-stop, I exited with my hands tingling from all the palm slapping. I needed another shower and hoped I'd be worn out enough to sleep through the heat.

My dance workout was effective; I only needed two cold showers during the night. I decided to mosey over to Nigerian Airways to check on my ticket. There were three lovely young ladies in red and yellow uniforms without shoes. I liked their style. I explained that I was waiting for a ticket from Italy for a flight from Kano to Rome. The girl smiled and said,

"I'll just take a look." She picked up about thirty official-looking pages, and half of them slid onto the floor. I helped her shuffle them back up. She slowly looked one by one, shaking her head, then at the bottom, she announced, "Here it is, Marie France Frontier." They misspelled my last name, but I claimed it.

I was gob-smacked that the ticket made it to Kano! I trusted Gio, but not the lackadaisical, unorganized, bureaucratic inefficiency of Italy or Nigeria. Another miracle, proving to me I had a creator who cared about details. It was fortunate I'd checked on the ticket this morning because my flight was in five hours. I zoomed back to my dumpy hostel, gathered my bags, and paid the bill. I decided it was more comfortable to chill out at the Palace Hotel for the next four hours, and then I'd leave for the Mallam Aminu Kano International Airport.

The six-hour flight to Rome went like clockwork. I arrived in The Eternal City at 8 pm, called Flavio from a telephone cabin, and allowed him to insist I stay at his place. We were awake to the wee hours since Flavio wanted to hear every single detail. I called Gio to thank him again for the awesome, "once in a lifetime trip," and the Nigerian Airways flight back to Rome. I reassured Gio that I still had his Nikon E12 35mm SLR Camera so that he could pick it up at Flavio's place. We had become great friends.

Gio was never demanding, macho, or arrogant - considering his family's prestigious status in Rome. We had the perfect platonic relationship. We avoided pushing each other's buttons; therefore, we meshed as ideal travel partners. I explained that I was off to Ibiza in a few days, and he invited me to meet him in London in several months. He had an architectural job to renovate an Italian bank in Knightsbridge, and I knew he needed help with English and someone to show him around. He'd get on well with my friends there, and I knew the best restaurants in London. "Yeah, Gio, London sounds great!" I gave him my shared postal box number in Ibiza.

I brought my Kano market treasures to Mama Loula's Boutique, and after haggling myself blue in the face, I exited unscathed with a tidy profit. I called the Alfa Modeling Agency to stay in touch and to let them know I'd be back sooner or later. After checking my mail at American Express, I passed by Angelo's boutique to reconnect with him and his wife Alona, and thank them again for setting up my job with Roberto Cavallini. I explained that he wanted me for his next season's fashion shows in about five months. All loose ends had been tied up. I was ready to head to Ibiza!

25. IBIZA, SPAIN

I found an early morning flight with Alitalia to Barcelona and a good connection on Iberia to the island of Ibiza. As I strolled towards the departure gate for Ibiza in the thick haze of the smoke-filled airport of Barcelona, I could just barely see a collection of hippie-types lounging around. They were united in their anticipation of returning to that jewel in the Med, IBIZA. I could tell that most of them lived there by their hippie garb, toting the island's logo, the Ibiza hand-woven unisex baskets made of strips of dried palm leaves. I started to feel at home already.

Just over an hour and we were bouncing to a stop on the rough asphalt runway, accompanied by applause and laughter. The miniature airport was covered with dark magenta bougainvillea in full bloom. It was inviting, despite the *Guardia Civil* (Civil Guard), who carried menacing weapons and wore fascist mustaches and three-cornered hats.

I shared a taxi with three multi-national hippies going to Ibiza town and found we knew many of the same people. I dragged my suitcase down to the port and made my way to *La Tierra*, the `in' bar. It was usually filled with draft-dodging Americans and the girls that followed. Adjoining *La Terra* (the earth) bar was *Los Caracoles* (The Snails) pension. It was an ideal spot to peer from a balcony onto the cave-like bar's patio and check out who arrived each evening. For sixty cents a night, I booked a room on the second floor with a perfect view of the bar below. Ibiza was one of the cheapest semi-civilized places in Europe.

As I skipped back to the main square to the Montesol Hotel, I scanned their popular outside street café for a familiar face. I felt like Cinderella and Ibiza was my glass slipper. It was a perfect fit. I felt more at home in Ibiza than I did anywhere else in the world. Charlie and Angie jumped up and were waving for me to join them. I worked my way with heartfelt hugs from table to table. Yes, I was home. Hmm, I was in the mood for a banana split. I had taught Juan, the handsome waiter, how to prepare the delectable dessert and discovered it was now on the menu. *Olé* !

Thinking back, it was here at the Montesol that I made a pact with Julian to share the gasoline costs to Morocco......and I never looked back. It had been over a year since I was sent out to the Far East by Ibizan friends with outlandish suggestions. I followed their fantasies and had become a catalyst for other dreamers to start on their journeys.

I was excited to get to the post office before it closed since I knew I'd have mail waiting for me. There were three letters from my mother and a manila envelope filled with letters she forwarded to me. Wow, a letter from Luke, the Jesus freak I'd met in Goa - also Vittorio, the Latin teacher I trekked with in Nepal, and Jonathan from Jerusalem. There was even a card from cryptic Barkley, who I spent the morning with inside The Great Pyramid of Giza. And yes, also letters from my soul mate Na Lin from Bali, my cousin Fran and my childhood friend, Becky. I walked back to my pension, where I could savor the letters and freshen up for an evening of fun at *La Tierra* bar below.

Na Lin said she was moving to Rome to be with Sandro, the photographer from Bali. Yay! We would reconnect on my next trip to Rome. Barkley reminded me to stay in touch and call when I arrived in London. Vittorio sent precious photos of Mahesh, my adopted boy, from Kathmandu. Sweet Vittorio, he remembered. My mother encouraged me to keep traveling and learning. She'd be in London the following summer and said we could take a trip together, perhaps to the famous Treetops Hotel in an animal reserve in Kenya. Cool, what an awesome mom.

My heart started to race as I opened the letter from Luke. He was back in Ohio and said he had another message for me. "Don't worry;

God will transform you from inside-out. Just lean on Him and trust Him. Get to know Him through His Word. The Holy Spirit will be your guide and your comforter. He will reveal God's Word to you. Jesus loves you." Tears trickled down my cheeks. Could it be true? I'd been such a rebel and traveled every wrong road. I was so egocentric. I didn't deserve it. That's what Luke tried to explain to me in Goa, and Jonathan echoed in Jerusalem - "It's not about your good works, it's about His grace."

It just occurred to me that Luke's message explained the *words* I received inside the King's Chamber. An inner voice spoke of being built from the inside out, and I thought that was for Barkley and Simon, referring to the King's Chamber. Oh, the message was for ME, and then the word YESHUA began reverberating over and over in my mind. The same *word* I received at Golgotha in Jerusalem with Jonathan. YESHUA - the Hebrew name for JESUS.

A floodlight of TRUTH washed over me, pinpointing the things I had to let go, but now I *wanted* to discard them. They didn't fit anymore. A recalibration of my heart was taking place; my entire being was coming into alignment with the Truth. I felt liquid love pouring into every crevice of my soul, touching those areas of hurt and anger and even melting unforgiveness. There was a balm of healing, a strength from within – but it was not my power. I was not alone, and I would never be alone. I invited Yeshua to stay with me forever. I needed Him. A paradigm shift had taken place.

Of all world religions, there was only one that included a Savior and only one extended *grace* – undeserved favor. I needed BOTH. The other religions I had studied were do-it-yourself salvation. You had to work your way to heaven with rules and regulations or else continue being reborn until you reached Nirvana. Then what? The *Gospel* (good news) offered me a complete clean-up and, above all, unconditional love that reached into eternity.

Like Mahatma Gandhi, I found Christ flawless; it was the Christians I objected to. What about the Spanish Inquisition and the Crusades? What about all the abusive clergy that are being indicted and hauled off to jail?

I could hear Luke's response, "Man is fallible. Jesus is not. Keep your eyes focused on JESUS." I remember clearly the feeling of being immersed in liquid love when Luke read out a verse for me. I felt that same immersion in the belly of the pyramid. I felt it in Jerusalem and under the star-filled heavens in the Sahara. I felt it NOW and hoped its intensity would NEVER fade.

Singing the Psalms brought me far more peace and joy than the Buddhist mantras or yoga meditations. My comfort came from the words in that pocket-sized Gideon Bible that Jonathan had given me and the companionship I now felt with God's Spirit. Jesus promised that he would `send the Holy Spirit' to his disciples after his departure - the Spirit of Truth, who would reveal all things.

Jonathan emphasized, "It's not about rules and regulations; it's about a RELATIONSHIP." Luke's verse for me was a prophecy that had been fulfilled, "Seek and you will find." I decided to believe God's rescue plan included me. I was in awe that Jesus would die for ME, so I could be set free and forgiven. My part was faith in His unconditional love and His promises. I knew Jesus had risen from the dead because I felt His presence. I would become a `follower of Jesus' without the trappings of man's traditions, and I would seek like-minded people.

I remember once hearing, you can't go back and restart the beginning, but you can change the ending. I had time - I was young. I still had a huge chunk of the world to see and things to do, but I decided to take YESHUA along with me. The trajectory of my life was changing course. However, I still longed to explore the Southern Hemisphere - to climb up to Machu Picchu and dance at the Carnival in Rio de Janeiro and perhaps travel down the Amazon. But I wouldn't be alone.

Jesus had become my Touchstone – my new standard - an example to aim for, to emulate. I knew myself too well - I often tried to run before

I could walk. I would try to take baby steps and realize that sometimes I might walk backward and often side-ways, but with my guide, the Holy Spirit, I would go forward. I decided to make it my life's journey.

I felt sure that Ibiza would become my home one day when it was the right time to settle down in one place, at least during the six month season. Ibiza may be just a frontier town now, but I could sense that it would become a boom-town with an ensuing gold rush. I wanted to participate in the upcoming opportunities. Most of the island's women could sew – it was a necessity in their self-sustainability. The farm women, tending their sheep and goats, also worked shoulder-to-shoulder with their husbands, cultivating crops and clothing their families.

Ibiza would be ripe in about five years. Meanwhile, I would continue developing my tribal jewelry business. I planned on making two trips a year back to Kathmandu, where I left part of my heart with Mahesh, the orphan boy. Then I would dip down to Jaipur, India, where the amazing desert nomads supplied my source of silver belts.

Modeling in the bi-annual fashion shows, which would boost my funds for further travels, was lined up with Roberto. The southern hemisphere was beckoning me.

Then back to IBIZA to ride the undulating wave of fashion, that would become a tidal wave! Boutiques, YES, I knew what would sell. I could organize a cottage industry to have my own designs manufactured on the island. Why not? It would enable women to work from their homes, draft patterns from my sketches, then cut and distribute the pieces of fabric to their neighbors to sew together. The dynamic, hard-working ladies of the island could become bread-winners while multi-tasking their farm duties at home. It would take vision and ingenuity for these ladies to help ensure university degrees for their offspring.

OK, I won't sugar coat my intentions, my goal will be to earn money, but I want to earn enough to give away a lot. I have been given so much, and I want to give back in every way. Most importantly, I won't be alone. I will invite JESUS into every area of my life. He will become my faithful travel companion and my business partner. He will become not only my Savior but my best friend. I will trust Him and not try to do it on my own. I can't.

I realize the term "MISFIT" usually has a derogatory connotation; however, the way I look at it, some of us are just too unique and too creative to fit into a conventional mold. It would stifle our creativity to conform to the structured 'norms' of society. Therefore God created unique places for us special people – to set us apart for His purposes. My place will be the island of Ibiza unless I get new instructions. I was relieved to discover that God loves misfits, and he has a place for each of us in His perfect plan. Our cracks allow His light to shine in. Do I have to grow up and leave behind my quirky, eccentric behavior? Do I have to start wearing boring clothes and hike my hair up into a neat bun? Do I have to outgrow my idiosyncrasies? Will I have to grow-up and act my age? I concluded – NEVER!

I unrolled the parchment scroll that Luke had given me in Goa and reread the last verses of the poem attributed to Sir Francis Drake:

"Disturb us, Lord, to dare more boldly,
To venture on wider seas
Where storms will show your mastery;
Where losing sight of land,
We shall find the stars.
We ask You to push back
The horizons of our hopes;
And to push into the future
In strength, courage, hope, and love."

Yes, I am convinced that I am meant to enjoy this journey that I am on called *life!* I found a verse in my pocket-sized Gideon Bible that Jon had highlighted, "Delight yourself in the Lord, and he shall give you the desires of your heart. Commit thy way to the Lord, trust also in him, and he shall bring it to pass." (Psalm 37:4-5) This Psalm became my song! It bubbled up into an effervescent melody that would accompany me wherever I went.

Well-meaning friends have advised me that traveling alone throughout South America is too risky, but I know that I will find the stars by losing sight of land. I feel led to venture on wider seas, knowing that storms will only show my creator's mastery. Besides, I am convinced that my well-traveled guardian angel is up for a new adventure.

I realize that life *is* a tapestry. Of course, I only see the reverse side of the weaving with lots of dangling threads. I'm tempted to pull out a few of those threads, but then the tapestry will unravel. I'll just have to trust my Creator, the master artist, and believe he is weaving a masterpiece.

The best is yet to come….stay tuned!

Nepal Elephant Camp

Kathmandu Orphan Boy Mahesh

Bangkok Temples

Bali

Egypt Caravan

Egypt Great Pyramides and Sphinx

Rome Photo Shoot

UNA PARTITELLA DISTENSIVA

Franco Interlenghi, tra... anonimi veneziani e la moglie Antonella Lualdi che non si sa se voglia divorziare o meno, ha certamente i suoi bei grattacapi ed è logico che qualche volta cerchi di svagarsi. Niente da dire, quindi, se i fotografi lo hanno scovato, in un campetto di periferia, mentre faceva una partitella al pallone con alcuni amici. Ha arbitrato la bella Tike Fortier (nella foto) attrice americana e amica, dicono gli informati, di Franco.

Rome Soccer With Stars

Spaghetti Western

Spaghetti Western Horse

Paris Modeling

Sahara Girls

Niger Dinosaur Guide

Ibiza

ABOUT THE AUTHOR

I am a full-time resident on the island of Ibiza, Spain (by choice)! After years of riding the undulating fashion wave, manufacturing my own designs on the island, and selling them in a trio of "Tyke" boutiques, I have embarked upon my `writing journey' with a humorous travel book. I've discovered that writing is not only addictive, but it is a divine excuse to avoid housework. However, I am cooking up a follow-up edition to "Banana Split Misfit." Stay tuned! You can contact me on the Destinee Media website: http://www.destineemedia.com/tyke-fortier.html

Printed by Amazon Italia Logistica S.r.l.
Torrazza Piemonte (TO), Italy

38213949R00154